To Sally

THE EMPTY
CARRIAGE

Published under licence by Brown Dog Books and The Self-Publishing Partnership, 7 Green Park Station, Bath BA1 1JB

www.selfpublishingpartnership.co.uk

ISBN printed book: 978-1-83952-199-7

Cover design by Kevin Rylands
Internal design by Andrew Easton

Printed and bound in the UK
This book is printed on FSC certified paper

THE EMPTY CARRIAGE

JUDYTH L GWYNNE

BROWN
DOG
BOOKS

Judyth L Gwynne is also the author of
The Illustrated Dictionary of Lace (Batsford, 1997)

This book is dedicated to Rowly Pillman, Bryan Stamp, John Bolitho, Maggie Perryman and Doreen Jones who all by their tireless efforts helped to bring Music and Music Therapy to the children of North Cornwall and North Devon.

'Let me not to the marriage of true minds
Admit impediments. Love is not love
Which alters when alteration finds,
Or bends with the remover to remove:
O, no! It is an ever-fixed mark,
That looks on tempests, and is never shaken:'

William Shakespeare. 1564–1616
Sonnet 116

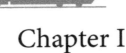

Chapter I
Overture

Elizabeth laid the newly made baby clothes, carefully wrapped in tissue paper, into the suitcase and closed the lid. She'd had so much fun making these small garments over the past few months, bringing into play old skills of knitting and embroidery. The taxi would arrive in a few minutes, so she ran around the house switching off the computer, after checking there were no messages here or on the phone, and scribbled a Post-it Note for her secretary before locking up and leaving the house. She smiled to herself as she carried out these now very familiar tasks – who would have thought that ten, no twelve years ago, someone who was, as her friends told her, an entrenched 'technophobe' would now be so comfortable with all these modern aids in her everyday life? She put on her coat and hat, ready now for the long journey to greet her new grandchild.

With all the business of taxi, coach and train connections she allowed her mind to drift back once again to her early morning thoughts – how did all this start, when was the moment that her life changed so completely and forever? Was it a word, a look, an event, which heralded the very beginning of this significant moment, propelling her into a new life with such speed and inevitability? If one believed in predestination, destiny, would she have been able to divert the onward progression of events? Maybe these thoughts were enhanced by the fact that the places along today's route awakened never to be forgotten memories which, despite occurring so long ago in time and distance, were still so fresh and vivid in her mind. She allowed her thoughts to drift dreamlike, as scene followed scene; when and where did it all begin? Perhaps her story really had no real beginning and no end as it was about love and immortality. But if it did have a beginning it probably came on one of the very last warm days of summer...

It is possible the words that set the wheels of destiny in motion were said by her ninety-year-old father one day as they sat together in the sunlit window of his flat overlooking the busy street below.

Sadly, her father's failing sight and hearing left him oblivious to the mild entertainment offered by passers-by, the children in chattering groups drifting home at the end of the afternoon. A few cars slowly passed by looking for a place to park in the nearby cul-de-sac, dogs sniffed happily at the interesting smells offered at each lamp post, a delivery van drew up at a neighbouring house. All everyday events repeated in different forms day on day, week on week. The scene varied very little, but the spare figure reclining in the wheelchair had his own thoughts to entertain him and on this particular day he abruptly looked across at the dimly seen form of his daughter, and said, 'You realise that if you die before me none of your children will inherit my money.' This startling statement, coming apparently unconnected to any prior conversation, jolted Elizabeth out of her own thoughts. It left her speechless, as her father up to this point had always avoided the subject of wills, or inheritances in any form, even if the topic had no direct relevance to him. In and her sisters had all learnt to avoid the subject as they knew how distasteful it was to him, and therefore really had given the matter very little thought. So, this very suddenly voiced remark left Elizabeth stammering and repeating his words, seeking assurance that she had correctly heard his startling statement.

'You mean that if any of us go before you our children will receive nothing, and the money will go to the remaining sisters?'

'That's right,' he replied firmly, offering no clarification and no opening for the discussion to continue. His spare, still dominant figure, that of a man brought up in the Edwardian mould, left her no room for any explanation or discussion, so to give herself time to think she left the table on the pretence of making an early cup of tea, her thoughts swiftly chasing one after the other. Elizabeth's ever practical self, reviewed this newly presented problem in her life as she put the kettle on to boil and loaded up the tray with cups and saucers. Her own means were small and her one constant fear was that she should leave her young family with little or no means of support before they were old enough to earn their own living. With the kettle now boiled she made the tea and carried the tray through to sit beside her father once again. Making him comfortable and popping several lumps of sugar into his tea, just the way he liked it, she managed despite his poor hearing to discuss all the arrangements for his prospective move from the flat to a new house nearby. A husband and wife had been found who would act as joint housekeepers and carers and would be living in separate accommodation on the top floor. It was most fortunate that all parties to this arrangement were pleased with this plan and her father seemed content with all that had been organised for his comfort. Elizabeth felt confident that she had done all she could on this visit to ensure a smooth transition on moving day.

With all these plans in place, it had been arranged that Elizabeth would be returning to her own home, a long day's journey to the West Country in two days' time. The day for travelling had been pre-arranged for that Saturday and she decided that by travelling a day earlier and breaking her journey, she could arrange an appointment with her solicitor. A plan was forming in her mind in which perhaps the three sisters could come to a legally binding arrangement that should any one of them pre-decease their father, their share would be given to their own children. It had to be faced that despite their father's present infirmities he could easily outlive them all as his mind was still very alert. He retained a strong interest in the world around him, and kept a firm hold on his own private financial interests.

A swift phone call confirmed the desired appointment in Exeter, and all that remained to do was to break the news to her father that she was needed at home and therefore would be leaving a day early. This rearrangement of course was necessitated by the fact that the lawyer's offices would not be open on the Saturday, her original day of travel. This news distressed the old man and although Elizabeth knew he would be cared for in her short absence she felt impelled to come to a swift arrangement with her two sisters, both residents in America, which would safely secure this, to her very surprising and completely unforeseen situation.

With many assurances that she would return a few days before the move and many hugs and kisses, she swiftly left the slightly forlorn figure behind, feeling torn by this most unexpected circumstance which made her early departure imperative.

So, on a still warm day, she left her father's home and entered the taxi which was to drive her to the station. When she arrived, the station seemed fairly busy with early morning travellers and so she stood with her luggage on the cool, shaded station platform and read the morning newspaper whilst she awaited her train.

That day she was still wearing her bright summer clothes with a red straw hat, a once smart relic of a visit abroad some years before. She knew this hat was becoming and as it gave her confidence in her late middle-aged looks, it had become a great favourite for summer wear. In fact, this hat had over many summers provoked many kind smiles and remarks: 'I like your hat!' from complete strangers as they passed by, so she felt she was not wrong in deciding once again to don her favourite headgear.

The train arrived on time and she settled into her seat prepared to enjoy the day-long journey which although tiring, would lead her ultimately into a new phase of her life. A pleasant smile hovered on her lips as she envisaged family visits, some travel maybe and peaceful hours spent in her beloved garden. With happy thoughts of this nature she viewed the passing scene which had become so familiar to her in the at times difficult, unhappy years of the past. How different her thoughts had been on those previous occasions when, responding to yet another urgent recall to duty, she had thrust back unworthy thoughts of the early hours, broken nights and uncomfortable conditions that awaited each arrival, with the querulous and sometimes demanding invalid who would greet her at each journey's end. On such journeys when these unwelcome thoughts had arisen, they were instantly quelled by loving thoughts of earlier, happier times. But as the years had progressed, she had found these calming meditations less easy to summon up and the weariness of never-ending demands was slowly eroding those dutiful thoughts to the point of a quiet suppressed anger. This anger increased her feelings of distress and general disquiet, and the resultant emotion of guilt such thoughts engendered only increased her misery at the situation she found herself in. What is more, she saw no apparent hope of an easy and satisfactory solution to her problem. In the past years no way out of her situation had presented itself and she had become accustomed to dealing with all these varied and mainly unwelcome feelings before presenting a smiling face and cheerful competent manner upon each arrival. It was this conflict of emotions which was causing her extreme exhaustion and ultimately reduced her this last time to face the fact that she no longer had the inner resources to continue; in fact, she felt that she had come to the end of her tether. Perhaps it was this unwillingly recognised fact that impelled her sisters to take definite action to relieve her of this burden before her usually robust health finally broke under the strain. Her love and gratitude to her sisters for their timely help could not be over-estimated and permitted her for the first time to believe that she could once again take joy in her own life without this shadow which threatened her love for her father. Possibly due to the physical infirmities imposed on him by old age, Elizabeth found it very hard to lighten the atmosphere in her father's home and she dreaded each return visit which caused her in the privacy of her own room to shed silent tears as she could see no end or solution to the never-ending problem.

At this stage in her thoughts she looked out onto the passing fields, now bare of harvested corn and noticed that some of the trees already had leaves with drying, curled edges foretelling the swift approach of autumn. Through the grubby window of the train she could see bright fruit ornamenting orchard trees and wild hedgerows, all passing before her reflective grey eyes.

Her mind once again fleetingly touched on all the problems of the past as they had been rehearsed over and over again in her mind. And she realised that maybe that she could now let go of these unhappy thoughts, she could now look forward to a new life free from the present stresses and strains. Perhaps now her earlier happier relationship with her father could re-establish itself. With this, lingering in her mind, she once more settled her plump matronly figure back more comfortably in the seat and for the first time that day started to relax. Stopping this drift of her thoughts of the past she enjoyed the luxury of a quiet uninterrupted read, mindful that at mid-day she would have to change trains at her first destination of Salisbury. It had become her custom there to treat herself to a cup of coffee and a Danish slice as her connection would be an hour later.

Her journey to Salisbury went smoothly and, as anticipated, the enjoyable refreshment at the station buffet made her feel both extravagant and almost verging on the holiday mood which had eluded her earlier in the day.

Sitting on the correct platform for the second leg of her journey, she surveyed the other passengers without any particular interest as they struggled with small children and huge piles of luggage. The younger travellers, apparently not minding the dirty platform floor, sat patiently around on their bulging back-packs drinking and eating. I wonder where they are all travelling to, she thought; some were obviously off on a walking holiday judging by their sensible boots with thick socks protruding from the tops. Older travellers relaxed in the filtered sunshine at little tables set out on the platform enjoying a moment's rest and refreshment. Her gaze travelled up to the roof trusses where earlier that month she had seen the station staff hanging large baskets of flowers along each platform, and now once again she appreciated the festive air this gave to the station.

While keeping an eye on the screen showing the train arrival and departure times, her attention was drawn to a station announcement which informed passengers that due to a very serious train crash the previous week, delays were inevitable and her train was therefore running twenty minutes late. With the luxury of a whole day before her, and no strict timetable to follow apart from the late afternoon appointment with her solicitor, this small irritation left her unmoved in light of the circumstances. With the ever-increasing number of potential travellers arriving on the platform, she moved her cases closer to accommodate those looking for a seat. Finally, on the approach of an elderly couple seeking a place to rest, she decided to get up and place herself in readiness at the platform's edge. She would have enough sitting all day, she reasoned with herself, and was glad to move around and watch for the approaching train as it came in sight round the corner into the station. The sunlight was so bright away from the shade created by the canopy that she put her sunglasses on to ease the strain of looking at the bright rails gleaming in the sun.

At long last the many carriages of her train came into view and stopped just as a voice on the tannoy announced its arrival. The rhythmic roar of the approaching train coming to a screeching halt almost completely obliterated the words. I wish they would not do that, she thought in slight annoyance at the amount of train announcements half-heard over the years.

Obeying a notice displayed on the platform which informed all travellers for Exeter to board the three rear carriages, she obediently struggled aboard with her heavy case and bag, and sat down. The train seemed very crowded and she congratulated herself on finding a vacant seat.

After waiting some time, she began to wonder at the cause

of the delayed departure and to her surprise saw more people struggling to get on, many of them coming from carriages further up the train. Supposing them to have got into the wrong part of the train she sat firmly in her seat, very glad to have found one in the circumstances. However, after a further delay she could just hear an announcement requesting all passengers who intended travelling to Exeter to now move to the front three carriages of the train. Not sure she heard this message correctly, she looked for confirmation from a lady sitting near the open carriage door who confirmed the fact, so Elizabeth got up and started to walk up the by now extremely crowded carriage way. Seeing not the slightest possibility of getting through from one carriage to another she decided to get out and do her best to sprint up the platform, laden as she was, hoping the train did not move off before she got to the other end. Out of breath, she threw herself into the last carriage but one and noting that this compartment was already completely packed with passengers, apologetically struggled through to reach the final carriage.

The first part of this compartment was full also, but halfway down she found to her surprise and relief two empty seats either side of the aisle, one to her left and one to her right. On the seat to the left sat a youth moodily staring out of the window, and to the right sat an older man with unusual dark aquiline features.

'May I sit here, or is the seat taken?' she asked. He shook his head gesturing towards the empty seat, and she settled thankfully into the place beside him.

In typically English fashion, as is often the case with the ice having been broken by the shared upset of their travel plans, they exchanged pleasantries. He told her that due to the major train crash the week before, his journey had been re-routed; normally he would not have been travelling on this particular train. He told Elizabeth that he was travelling from his home in London to his holiday destination in the south of Cornwall.

After a slow start they soon began to talk on a wide range of subjects and it came to light that he had in years past taught at a famous school of music in London but that now his main interest was in photography. With her co-passenger seated sideways beside her she could not really get a good look at him; although not young, she found his mind was open and engaging. In the most natural fashion, he told her of his close family losses in the past year and this, together with a failed personal relationship, made him seem in her eyes a saddened and lonely man. She warmed to this interesting fellow passenger, and during their two hours of conversation which rarely seemed to falter between one subject and another, she became aware that interested eyes were on them and looked up. At once her eyes met those of a pleasant couple seated facing them on the other side of the carriage, who had undoubtedly witnessed the meeting – the meeting of two total strangers. Their faces expressed their astonishment at this engrossed man and woman freely airing their views on travel, the arts and music in particular, among many other subjects, agreeing that they thought the Welsh choirs were wonderful. The time passed for them incredibly quickly despite the fact that the journey was over half an hour longer due to the inevitable delays along the line after their late departure from Salisbury.

Throughout the entire conversation she had been unable to see much of her companion's face except his profile, due to the restrictive seating arrangements. However, she noted without much undue interest, that he was dressed in a light grey waterproof jacket, and conventional trousers, none of which could be termed smart but which were obviously serviceable.

As their conversation progressed it seemed to her that he had a need to unburden himself and she noticed that at first, he was not at all curious about her and her life. She was perfectly happy for him to do this as she instinctively felt his need and gave herself up to listening to him, just making the odd remark as the occasion required. His relaxed and natural behaviour endeared himself to her when he mentioned that he had a hole in the lining of his jacket and demonstrated it by putting his finger through it. 'It could be mended,' offered Elizabeth tentatively, hoping that she did not have to deal with such a repair herself but he just closed his jacket and made no comment.

It was with some surprise and regret the realisation dawned on her that the journey's end was fast approaching and they would soon have to say goodbye. During their conversation she told him a little about herself, that she earned a small living by writing articles and had produced some very modest booklets on various subjects relating to the arts. He volunteered the fact that his cousin was employed by a publishing firm and could possibly help her place her more recent work. He surprised and pleased her when he said he would put her on his Christmas card list and so they exchanged business cards. He carefully read through her card and asked if he could address her by her Christian name, and this being agreed, volunteered his own, Michael.

Michael, as she hesitatingly called him, told her that when he saw her coming through the train looking for a seat, he had thought to himself, 'She looks a bit of alright,' which amused her greatly. Although a slightly old-fashioned unadorned compliment, from him it seemed totally inoffensive. At the same time, he confessed he particularly liked her hat, adding, 'I nearly got my camera out to photograph you!' which again caused her to smile. Without thought she told him, 'I'm very glad you didn't, how embarrassing!' but nevertheless followed this remark with another smile.

As the train halted at the, to her, very familiar platform at Exeter station she got up from her seat and started to struggle down the crowded aisle when he called out her name, 'Elizabeth!' with some joking remark about helping with the luggage. She turned for a last wave and joined the queue of passengers waiting to alight.

Out in the midday sunshine, to her surprise she found him jumping out behind her, and they stood on the platform to say goodbye once again. For some reason she could never explain she felt a sense of regret at parting from this quiet, friendly, unassuming man and put out her hand to formally shake his before turning to go. As she walked down the length of the platform, she wished the journey could have been much longer.

Chapter II

Entr'acte

Elizabeth, Liz or Lizzie as she was generally known to her friends, spent a busy time on her return home after an absence of several weeks. There seemed to be so much to do before she would be returning in ten days to assist with her father's removal to his new home.

There was a great deal of correspondence to clear up and various mundane jobs such as paying bills and getting the lawn cut. During these very active days her thoughts did wander upon occasion to her companion on her recent railway journey and she wondered if he was enjoying his holiday at the furthest tip of Cornwall. He had told her he always carried his camera wherever he went, so no doubt in the lovely weather of that week he would have ample opportunity to take many pictures. Her mind went back to that shared journey, and on reflection it seemed it was as if they had been in some sort of time capsule, barely registering, if at all, the various station stops along the way, or the alighting and boarding passengers brushing past them, so engrossed were they in their conversation.

As she sat down late in the week to put her correspondence in order, she decided, with some trepidation, that it perhaps would not be too extraordinary to write a civil line asking him if he remembered her as a fellow traveller and if he would not mind her taking him up on his offer to provide her with the address of his contacts in the publishing trade, allowing her to submit the manuscript they had discussed on the train. On a lighter note at the end of the letter she said, 'I should warn you I am travelling back to Sussex on Thursday next week and return five to six days later, so don't go sitting next to ladies with hats! You never know where it might lead you!' Not at all sure she had struck the right note, she added below this paragraph that she would quite understand if he did not wish to be involved in her publication affairs and there was no necessity to send a letter in reply, firmly signing herself at the end of the page with a flourished *Elizabeth*. She sealed the envelope and decided not to post it until the next day to allow her to change her mind in the meantime. This was a habit with her as she had come to rely on her second thoughts as usually being the best. Elizabeth remembered that Michael had told her he was going to be away for two weeks so any delay in sending her letter would not matter at all.

Next day she decided he could always ignore the letter if he wished, so she posted it off. Her nature was usually rather shy and retiring and never in her life had she ever initiated a relationship of this kind; her boldness on this occasion left her feeling rather surprised at herself.

All too soon the return to duty meant another day-long journey back to Sussex. This time the journey was uneventful, but at the back of her mind she held a tiny scrap of hope that a letter would be awaiting her on her return home.

All thoughts of her own life went on hold as she helped with the difficult move and, after sleeping on a narrow camp bed near her father for a few nights in case he became distressed in his new surroundings or wandered out of bed, she felt confident that the smooth transition to the carers' own routine could be left safely in their hands.

As the days passed, she began to feel, if anything, rather in the way with the new household arrangements taking place around her and so, with a thankful heart, she realised she was at last free to go. Her father was wheeled to the front door for their goodbyes, holding her hand for a lingering moment and asking for a firm promise to come back in a month's time. Assurances were immediately given and with a swift kiss on the lean cheek, Elizabeth hurried out the door. This goodbye left her with an uncomfortable feeling of unease and she regretted her decision to depart comparatively early, but nevertheless had been very surprised at how well the ninety-year-old had coped with the upheaval and was apparently settling into his old accustomed routine. On reflection she decided that perhaps he was actually enjoying having two people at his beck and call instead of the normal daily help. The couple looking after her father had promised to contact her immediately should his health take a turn for the worse so, with many other assurances that everything was now being done and would be done in the future to ensure his comfort and care, she took one more look at the figure at the door and then felt able to give a last wave as the car drove off down the street. This goodbye today had given her a pang reminiscent of the heartbreak of leaving her young children at boarding school so many years ago but Elizabeth knew that this move and all it entailed had been in keeping with her father's own wishes and with this she had to be content for the moment.

The return journey went smoothly with all her connections made in good time. At Salisbury station her mind re-wound like an old film, to her surprise remembering every detail of her meeting with the stranger on the train. I wonder if I will ever see him again, she thought, and realised that apart from a well-remembered profile silhouetted against the brightly sunlit window of the train, she really could not recall how he looked either in stature or feature. Maybe there will be a letter, she mused, and allowed her thoughts to drift into pleasant daydreams.

It was to be another three weeks before she knew the answer to those dreams.

Chapter III

Pausa

This time the return trip home allowed Elizabeth to get down to some serious writing. With her bank balance much depleted, and mindful of the necessity of selling some of her articles, she structured her days to ensure several hours of each were employed in augmenting her small pension.

At this time no letter was received from her solicitor and therefore one nagging worry remained in her mind: I must not get run over by a bus, she half ruefully told herself. However, her sisters were now fully informed of the situation of any of them pre-deceasing their father they would all honour their joint verbal agreement and see that any children involved would receive their mother's third share. After her interview in Exeter she was not hopeful that a legal document could be drawn up to this effect and it was on point she was waiting for this particular letter.

As the weeks had passed with no reply to her letter to Michael, she had reasoned with herself, producing many excuses and probabilities as to why no answer had been forthcoming, eventually arriving at the conclusion that the matter had ended and she would hear no more. Reasonably enough she had specifically stated in her letter there was no need for a reply, and therefore it was best to let the matter drop and concentrate on other things.

Not long before this meeting with Michael she had had a young friend to stay, the son of old friends who needed a bed for a few nights whilst he visited his old father, at present residing in a nursing home nearby. Elizabeth had known the family for a great many years; all of them had been very good to her and her children especially in the period of her divorce. This friendship had lasted for nearly 30 years and had now been extended into the next generation.

Elizabeth's policy with her guests was to provide a warm bed and feed them well, indicating that they were free to amuse themselves how they wished. If they wanted to include her in their walks or excursions, she was pleased but, not wanting to relinquish her self-imposed work schedule too much, this arrangement suited her very well. It seemed her guests found her easy-going attitude to their liking, as many return visits were made by her wide circle of friends.

On this particular evening her young friend sat at ease after a good supper and while sharing a bottle of wine he had brought her, and as often before, they started to discuss deep matters of life, politics and religion. With the ease of old friendship she felt able to frankly put forward her own views which, although not as radical as his, were always first listened to politely, and then fiercely counter-argued as was his custom, to the enjoyment of both – this sharpening of their minds on each other being part of that enjoyment.

By the end of the evening the subject fell to a lighter mood with the question posed to her – which specific characteristics or features did she regard as the most attractive in the opposite sex?

It has to be said Elizabeth had not for many years given any specific thought to this subject, but after a moment's serious consideration she slowly replied, 'I think it has to be the mind; physical attributes are not at all important.'

Before the words were barely out of her mouth, he laughed her words to scorn, and tried to pin her down to specifics such as height, colouring or even more pertinently some part of the person's anatomy! After some more heated debate, while he enumerated the charms of different girlfriends, she stuck to her point, and wound up her argument by saying that after having lived alone for so long she had quite given up any idea of meeting her perfect man, and had thought in fact that he did not exist. They finished the bottle of wine falling, as they so often had in the past at the end of each discussion or argument, into laughter and agreed as always to disagree.

The next day, after he waved goodbye and she had shut the door, the house seemed very quiet without his presence. How I enjoy the company of young people, she thought, and was appreciative that they considered her company worth keeping.

It was one Tuesday morning that the postman delivered her mail and amongst the leaflets and bills, together with other unwanted post, lay a long white envelope addressed in an unknown hand in black ink. Noting the postmark, she felt confident that this was a letter from Michael. Not at all sure how her direct approach had been received she eagerly opened the envelope and swiftly scanned the large pages covered in a firm hand. On noting that the letter commenced with 'Dear Elizabeth' and closed at the bottom of the second page by him sending his 'Sincere Regards' and signed with his name 'Michael', she settled back into a comfortable chair, by now feeling quite confident that the easy talk in the train was to be extended in his pleasant letter.

Michael wrote, 'I returned from my travels only a few days ago.

The perfect weather influenced me to stay longer than originally intended.' She read on, happy now that the delayed reply was fully explained. 'When finally I arrived home last week I found among the bills and brown envelopes, your letter. Thank you. I've decided not to heed your warning about sitting next to ladies with hats – why should you deny me the pleasure of compatible company again?' At this point in his letter she giggled girlishly to herself as she read on. 'The diversity of subjects we discussed certainly erased the tedium of a long journey and instead of me, I'm sure if it had been Renoir you had sat next to, the art world would have a new masterpiece: "Une femme avec un Chapeau!"' Her laughter broke out at this absurdity and without a break she continued to read over the page which gave further news of his holiday. He had added his cousin's address and told her he had already discussed the matter of publishing her work with him on his return home, and so would be expecting to hear from her if she wished to pursue the matter further. The letter ended with a simple, 'So nice to have met you, Elizabeth'.

After re-reading this long-awaited letter several times, she put it aside with a mixture of feelings.

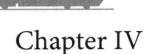

Chapter IV
Concord?

The next week, feeling somewhat diffident, Elizabeth decided to send her manuscript to Michael's cousin, and promptly by the end of the week she received a reply saying he had passed it over to a publishing company who might be interested. This expeditious attention to her letter pleased Elizabeth enormously and led her into hopeful thoughts that with this type of direct contact she might well be successful in getting this work and even others published.

Elizabeth now felt herself to be in a quandary regarding whether she should again make any response to Michael's reply to her first letter, received over a week ago now. However, this was resolved in the following week while she was under the hair dryer when the telephone rang. Sticking her head out of the hood she took the call and heard a voice she remembered from before saying 'Hello Elizabeth, just a quick call, my cousin has been on the phone and says your girlfriend is costing me money: there were no stamps on the letter she sent me!' Puzzled and mystified, she told him she could only presume they had fallen off and promised to immediately send a refund in the next post. The call was soon over as Michael seemed busy and he rang off. It was many years since Elizabeth had been called anyone's 'girlfriend' and she enjoyed this remark with some amusement.

Upon reflection, Elizabeth decided to write just one more letter to once again establish communication with her friend, a communication she was beginning to feel was becoming important to her. Accordingly, she sat down to write one of her chatty letters, firstly informing him that the all-important refund of stamps had been sent to his cousin, and, thanking him for putting them in touch, she promised to keep him informed of any progress in the matter. Following Michael's lead in telling her about his holiday she went on to describe her garden, and explained how important it was to her as a source of refreshment and strength. As she wrote she mentioned happy family tea parties in the summer months when friends were invited to sit under the apple trees and eat her homemade cakes and possibly indulge in the local speciality of Cornish splits with jam and clotted cream. At the conclusion of the letter she mentioned that she would be taking one of her grandchildren for a two-week holiday abroad and she would send him a card from there. As an afterthought she popped a recent photograph of the house and garden into the envelope so he could have some idea of her environment, which she had been describing to him in her letter.

At this time, both before and after this letter was sent, she was not at all sure that their friendship was anything other than that of passing acquaintances, and would in the following months just naturally fizzle out. But she could not stop thinking about the cumulative accidents and coincidences of their first meeting; she travelling a day earlier than intended, he being on her train because of a disruption to services caused by a major train crash, and then finally her boarding at one end of the train, the opposite end to where he was sitting, and then at the final moment being re-directed to end up sitting next to him. Just dimly seen, but already felt, was a feeling that destiny was taking over her thinking in relation to this man.

At this moment she was not at all prepared for a change in her life; she knew herself to be exhausted and needing peace and quiet to recuperate her strength after the, at times, strenuous nursing duties of the past five years. By now she was really not sure if she wished to receive another letter, but her race to retrieve the post from the postman gave away the feelings she had told herself she didn't have.

Finally, after what felt like a long ten days, that long white envelope with the firm black writing fell through the letter box. Swiftly opening it she found it full of fun, as before causing smiles as she read nonsense lines interspersed with appreciative remarks about her garden picture and descriptive passages. He went on to tell her all about his family, his parents both gone as he had told her on the train. The lives of both his parents were immensely interesting to her, and he added that he was sure she would have got on very well with his mother as their interests would have coincided. The letter concluded with a promise to send her copies of the photographs taken on his Cornish holiday. He completed his letter by wishing her an enjoyable break away, saying he would be pleased to know how she fared, signing himself, 'Sincerely Michael'.

Chapter V

Intermezzo

The planned holiday in Bruges was a great success and Elizabeth and her granddaughter Joanna enjoyed themselves immensely walking along the canals and choosing a different restaurant each day where delicious fish dishes featured prominently in the menus.

One morning they sat in the sun at the café table enjoying not only good coffee but also large slices of rich gateaux.

'I really don't know how on earth I shall get through this!' said Elizabeth, and noted her usually hungry granddaughter was also finding her portion more than enough to cope with. As they sipped their coffees, they wrote their postcards to friends and family, holding up each selection to discuss which would most suit each particular person on their list. Amongst Elizabeth's pile of cards was one addressed to Michael – this card she had slipped in without any previous discussion with Joanna.

One of the reasons they had chosen Bruges as a venue for their holiday was an introduction to a distant kinsman, and accordingly they had telephoned him to say they had arrived, giving the name of their hotel. Before departure Elizabeth had written ahead to re-introduce herself and remind him of their connection through marriage. The response to her letter had, it has to be said, caused her some amusement, as he had included in his reply a photograph of himself asking her if she liked what she saw.

The meeting with the relation was arranged and upon his arrival they all sat down to drinks in their hotel before going in to dinner. Elizabeth had no difficulty in recognising the stranger as he looked exactly like his photograph. They all chatted easily about mutual relations, passing on up-to-date information about their extended family, seemingly scattered all over the world.

Whilst enjoying their after-dinner coffee, her kinsman became very confidential and confessed that he was now living alone as both his mother and father had died that year. How strange, Elizabeth thought to herself – he is in exactly the same situation as her new friend on the train.

Before they exchanged continental embraces and kisses on both cheeks on his departure, he enquired into the details of their programme for the remainder of the week. He said he would like to join them on a trip up the canal and give them his local knowledge of the interesting places they would see. As this boat trip was already on their agenda Elizabeth and Joanna were happy to have such a congenial companion as their guide and so final arrangements were made.

The canal trip provided a different perspective to their view of the lovely city they were enjoying more every day. The embarkation site was so pretty with pots of yellow and mauve pansies lining the windows and beside the tall houses along the canal. Their rendezvous was at the Fish Market where motor boats waited to fill up with the next queue of expectant sightseers. After what seemed a long wait, their boat was filled up to the boatman's satisfaction and they set off for their tour of the canals. Both Elizabeth and Joanna had brought their cameras with them and snapped away happily away as each subsequent and apparently more attractive piece of mediaeval architecture came into view. Their self-appointed guide was most interesting and all enjoyed each other's company, laughing and talking like old friends.

After the crowded boat their attentive kinsman suggested some refreshments and, nothing loath, they all headed for the nearest cafe/bar where he gallantly ushered them into their seats.

Whilst they sipped their lemon tea the easy talk took on a more serious note as he told Elizabeth he was looking for a wife to look after him in his old age. Not daring to look at her granddaughter, Elizabeth could not resist encouraging him to enlarge on this theme, hoping her sense of humour could be kept in check, by asking what type of person he was looking for. With all seriousness he replied he would like to find someone who could talk as she did on a variety of interesting subjects – but younger!

Looking back to that afternoon later in the day when they had regained their hotel room, the two women, the young and the old, collapsed on their beds in laughter, at last giving rein to their repressed desire for giggles at this frank admission of the ideal wife required by a soon-to-be retiring gentleman.

'I suppose,' Elizabeth said mopping the tears from her face as another wave of laughter threatened to engulf her again, 'I am surprised he did not offer *you* the post of wife/nurse right away!' Whereupon the pair made a dash for the box of paper handkerchiefs to mop up more tears of laughter as they cascaded down their cheeks.

'Just look at my make-up,' they said simultaneously, and sobering down decided to do some serious tourist type shopping before their departure the next day. They spent the remainder of the day in the chocolate and lace shops, enjoyably purchasing small gifts for those at home.

This holiday really made Elizabeth feel young again, and she felt ready for whatever lay ahead.

Chapter VI

Crescendo

The week after their return from holiday Elizabeth slipped once again back into her now established routine of work, fitting in at the same time some early preparations for Christmas. This year she was making extra cakes and puddings for the family as well as preparations of her own to entertain old friends and neighbours during the Christmas and New Year holiday. With this in mind an early start seemed a good idea, and so one grey afternoon she laid out all her ingredients to make the first of the large cakes. The best occupation for such a dull day, she thought as she spooned the brandy-soaked fruit into the cake mixture and smelt the delightful aroma of beaten eggs, butter and sugar combined with the nuts and fruits.

It has to be admitted her thoughts were not entirely with her cake making as she had had a telephone call from Michael the night before in which they had talked and talked for over an hour, as on the previous occasion on the train, covering a wide range of subjects.

'You sound as though you are right here,' he had said, and she answered, 'You sound as though you are beside me on the sofa.' He then went on to tell her that he was receiving electric shocks from her letters, and finally she had to admit that she felt as if she had been struck by lightning.

'This is all new territory to me, I am really a shy person you know,' he answered.

'It is to me too,' Elizabeth hastened to say truthfully, feeling as though the innermost core of her being was shaken and stirred up. He spoke of what he called her 'sweet letters', adding 'you are so understanding'.

'Do you like my scribbles?' she asked.

'Yes, keep writing,' he encouraged her.

At this moment she re-adjusted the telephone to a more comfortable position as her hand was growing numb after their long conversation, and by mistake hit the redial button on her receiver. Not knowing what had caused the sudden silence, she re-dialled his number. After a moment they were re-connected.

'What happened, what happened?' he sounded very concerned, possibly thinking she had hung up the telephone on purpose. Having reassured each other on this point, they went on talking for a few more minutes.

'Do you realise I have never seen you properly? I can just remember your profile on the train; I would like to see you again one day.'

His firm, emphatic 'No' to her question left her both puzzled and surprised.

Despite his refusal for them to meet again, all she could remember when the phone went down was the way their minds seemed to mesh, the happiness of their concord causing her to giggle rather a lot while they talked. Her remark to Michael that she felt as though she had been struck by lightning only just described how she was feeling. After having given up all hope of finding the perfect man for her she had found him; her feelings were in turmoil. The timing was not good from her point of view as she hoped to catch up on a great deal of work which was absorbing her at the moment, and now here today she was trying to make a Christmas cake when in fact she had not the slightest idea what she was doing. Her fears that all the expensive ingredients would be wasted in an unprecedented 'flop' made her wish she had not decided to make such a large cake when her feet were not even touching the ground.

It was at this moment, the oven on and the cake receiving its last turns with a metal spoon, when the doorbell rang. Quickly wiping her fingers on a handy cloth, she presented herself at the door, the words of apology on her lips for doing so wearing her apron.

The lady at the door was an acquaintance met in the past over some charitable work. She was formally dressed and held a clipboard and briefcase under her arm. 'How nice to see you,' Elizabeth said, wondering why she had called, and ushered her into the house explaining how she was just in time to stir the cake and make a wish. Laughing together they entered the kitchen, and after their separate ceremonial stirrings of the cake mixture, and silent wishes, her visitor seated herself at the table and watched as Elizabeth turned the large mixture carefully into the already prepared tin and then proceeded to carefully load it into the hot oven.

The two women were of similar age, the other some four or five years younger. She explained she was doing a survey for a firm and would Elizabeth give her some time to answer some questions?

'I'll just make us both a cup of tea and then I can pay attention,' was the answer as they seated themselves informally at the kitchen table.

To Elizabeth's surprise the survey took quite a long time to complete and although there was a serious intent behind it, she was swiftly guided through the, at times, not so easy questions remaining to be answered. After all the questions had been dealt with and the papers put away in the briefcase, they both relaxed with their hot cups of tea. Somehow the conversation slipped from the usual pleasantries into a more personal area and Elizabeth was told how the lady's husband had been much comforted and helped by a visit to a palmist relating to a problem that had been worrying him for some time.

She went on to say, 'It is very helpful, my husband told me; if there is something bothering you, or you feel you need some guidance for the future, I can really recommend it.'

Elizabeth demurred, 'I really cannot feel happy with all that sort of thing. I feel it is best not to know the future, is it not frowned upon by the Church?'

'My husband felt the same as you, but there was no unpleasant mumbo-jumbo with all the trappings of an occult nature; his visit certainly set his mind at rest,' and seeing Elizabeth's doubtful expression she added, 'You know they are not allowed to tell you anything bad to frighten or worry you.'

Elizabeth asked her new friend if she had many more people in the street to interview that day, and was told that she was the only one chosen in the area, so she was finished for the day. I wonder why she chose me, Elizabeth thought to herself.

After her friend had gone, Elizabeth pondered over their conversation, the words that her visitor's husband had been much helped and comforted by the interview with the palmist stuck in her mind. Without acknowledging the fact to herself, over the past few days she was becoming drawn to the idea of some guidance regarding where her so very new relationship with Michael might be leading. She seemed to be getting conflicting messages from him which she found slightly confusing; his word 'No' to her enquiry if they could meet some time was still echoing in her ears.

She felt reluctant to confide in family or friends, mainly because, she reasoned with herself, she was not at all sure how they would view the idea of someone on the wrong side of sixty-five falling so irrevocably in love. No, she corrected herself, I am not 'in love' – I love this man, it is not the same thing at all. The idea of physical love did not seem to enter her thinking at this time.

During these days of silent thought, whilst her hands were busy with household and gardening tasks, she ruminated on the subject of love, and realised the present overwhelming feelings did not fit into any emotions previously felt in her long life.

She could well remember a conversation she had had with her father when a young woman of seventeen or eighteen. They were on a journey in the car and the intimacy of the close confinement of the vehicle gave her courage to raise the subject of love and how she was to know when the real thing came along. Her father was somewhat taken aback by this type of conversation with his young daughter and had finally, after some thought, come up with the not too helpful words, 'You will just know'.

Elizabeth, however, persisted. 'How will I just know?'

'You will just know,' was all he would reiterate, and ended the subject there, leaving her feeling even more confused than before. Of course, she had been attracted to various young men, at one point even becoming engaged, but luckily for their future happiness that had been broken off. Some years later a very strong physical attraction had led her into marriage and children. Looking back down the years she had been so very sure at the time that this was the 'real thing' her father had promised, but she had now come to realise rather sadly that although these were at the time overwhelming feelings of 'being in love' she was now able to recognise it as being a physical state alone, admittedly allied to feelings of friendship, which had remained to the present day.

Now the scale and range of emotional feeling that engulfed and astonished her seemed to have lifted her on to a plane of intense experience un-guessed at – leading her into a new realm which opened up to her an incredible range of emotion. She had not imagined it was possible to have such feelings of love for someone who was almost a total stranger. Her resolve was to only bring happiness into his life after his sad past if he would allow her.

Suddenly all the writings of the mystics with their descriptions of different aspects of pure love were now revealed to her; before this time, she could honestly say their words held very little meaning and were probably dismissed by her as poetic flights of fancy. Again her mind pursued the thought that their meeting had been part of destiny, and despite all the cautions put forward by her mind, her heart unbidden began to sing. Unbidden also came dreams of a possible future of great happiness which kept a gleam of sunshine coming into her heart. She instinctively knew that in some way Michael and she belonged together. Her only shadow at present was his refusal to see her again perhaps like her he was afraid of happiness, that precious possession was too much to hope for, or maybe old hurts and anxieties he had experienced in the past, which he had only briefly alluded to when they first spoke on the train, had made him very cautious in forming new relationships.

Having trodden this course in her meditations over and over again, Elizabeth knew she had to speak to someone who did not know her, and it was at this point, with some trepidation, she decided to make an appointment with the palmist recommended to her by her visitor some days before.

Chapter VII

Development on a Theme

Elizabeth had almost decided to cancel her appointment with the palmist and although feeling rather foolish, she finally went into the shop where crystals and other objects were displayed for sale. Burning joss sticks, accompanied by a very pungent smell of different types of potpourri, made her feel a little sick. All her worst fears of the wisdom of keeping this appointment seemed confirmed; to make matters even more worrying, the owner of the shop ushered her into a tiny back room and after explaining the palmist was running a little late due to heavy traffic on the road, shut the door.

Elizabeth looked around the room and sat down on one of the two small wooden chairs, the sole furniture in the room except for an equally small, round table. The walls were bare except for one or two old posters; in fact, the place looked more like a box room, obviously at present used as an office, than a scene for delving into the supernatural. It was the very ordinariness of the room which made her decide to sit patiently and wait.

Before Elizabeth had left home, she had originally decided to remove her wedding ring, but on second thoughts, and she was good at these, felt that wearing it would not really give such a good clue to her exact status at the time. Nevertheless, she had dressed simply, not wishing to give any pointers to her occupation to the lady who was supposedly able to tell her all about herself. In fact, she had no intention of giving away by word or gesture the slightest clue that might help with the reading of her hands. She was so determined on this point that as soon as the slim young woman, dressed in faded jeans and an old pullover, entered the room, Elizabeth made it perfectly clear that she would make no comment whatever during the reading, and would confine herself at the end of the hour long session to telling her if she had been right or wrong in the matters disclosed.

Despite these strictures the palmist happily agreed with this arrangement and sat herself down on the chair opposite Elizabeth, taking hold of her right hand and turning it over to face palm upwards.

The shop bell kept ringing outside their little room, and the loud voice of the shopkeeper could be heard intermittently, which caused the young woman to say it was interfering with her concentration.

The palmist carefully traced the different lines of Elizabeth's hand, turning it to one side and another in order to see the lines more clearly. She was able to speak of past events with great accuracy, Elizabeth having no doubt that the details could not possibly be common knowledge. The significance of many of the events she told of her past she had not divined for herself, but on these being pointed out to her she realised the truth of the statements.

Careful to say nothing at all, either by smiling or showing any other emotion on her face, she relinquished her right hand and as requested obediently produced the left from her lap. As before, the palmist looked at the hand for several minutes before speaking. At this point Elizabeth could not resist breaking her self-imposed vow of silence.

'How can you see all these things?'

'It is coming from you,' was the reply, an answer which surprised Elizabeth but interested to hear further about her future, she lapsed into silence, fearing to break the concentration shown by her companion of the little back room. By this time, she was also becoming increasingly impressed by the calm manner and the signs of professionalism in which this interview was being conducted.

Later Elizabeth could not remember the exact sequence of the words said to her, but she was told she should have a connection with music and with emphasis repeated her words, 'You really should do something about your music'. She was also told, 'You will have a library, and you will soon be meeting someone special. This special person will stay with you forever; he will go wherever you go.'

While Elizabeth digested this interesting news the palmist continued, 'You will be attending a family reunion overseas and do a lot of travelling abroad, I see tall thin trees and mountains, and this person you will soon meet will be there with you. This man you will meet very soon, will be by your side forever, no later than six months' time. No,' she corrected herself, 'maybe earlier than that, it could be five months.'

The reading over, Elizabeth allowing her usual reticence regarding her personal life to go to the winds, found herself confessing to the interested young woman that all she had been told of the past was quite correct. She then went on to give her an outline of past events mentioned and their subsequent results. Speaking of the future she could not stop herself from saying she thought she had already met the person whom the palmist had seen and he had a strong connection with music.

'That is absolutely perfect for you,' the palmist said, 'that is the connection with the music in you.' Elizabeth warmed to the unassuming air of this young person who gave her such happy and thought-provoking news.

As they shook hands at the end of the interview, the young woman said she was so interested in her reading that she would like Elizabeth to return in a year's time to see how things had turned out for her. She went on to explain that not many times did she have such an interesting palm to read and she could not help being intrigued at how her story would end.

Driving home, Elizabeth's mind dwelt on the two points of particular interest to her, the first that Michael would be with her in not later than six months' time – by now she felt so sure he was indeed the 'special person' mentioned in her interview – and the palmist's insistence he would be with her always wherever she went. The last part of the prediction she found a little odd; how was it at all possible for him to be with her wherever she went? No relationship she had ever experienced flourished without some time apart in their joint lives, be it only an hour or two in the day. However, these words were never to leave her thoughts through all the events of the next months. The final result at the time was impossible for her to imagine it seemed that all the long years of loneliness and unhappiness were now to end and for the first time she began to believe that at last real happiness might be in store in the near future.

That week, with many of her questions answered by her interview with the palmist, she received a long telephone call from Michael, again in the evening as before. He revealed that he did not like giggling girls, and Elizabeth remembered their first call when, she now blushed to remember, her giggles of happiness kept bubbling up as their minds matched on all the subjects they discussed. She told him that she seemed to be writing letters to him in her head, an explanation of the continual stream of thoughts she felt she wanted to share with him.

While they talked of his holiday in Cornwall, he promised to send her his photographs taken on this trip. He had promised to send these to her before, but he has been so busy with other photographic work. During their conversation he also promised to come and stay with her and went on to tell her he was thinking of selling his house in London and moving down to the South, possibly even to Cornwall. They discussed different areas of the country that would still enable him to keep in touch with possible photographic assignments. They remarked that with new technology many people were now able to work from home, so the exact location of a home was no longer so important.

As on previous occasions they both seemed reluctant to put the phone down, and as before Elizabeth made sure that she was the one to say goodbye first, their hour-long conversation seeming like minutes, so fleetingly passed.

Elizabeth surprised herself at this time by the boldness of her letters and discussions over the telephone, so out of character from her usual shy and diffident self. However, now a very strong inner certainty had been developing within her as this relationship progressed that she could share her innermost thoughts and feelings without either embarrassment or misunderstandings.

Getting to know each other through their letters and conversations was the happiest of times, with many vistas opening up of even more possible happiness in the future. It seemed their accord in almost all things was complete.

Chapter VIII

Discord

By now, through their long telephone conversations, Elizabeth was almost completely sure that her feelings and those of Michael were the same; she knew the time had now come when she would have to confide in her children. After their initial surprise they were, to her relief, entirely supportive.

'You do realise that we may end up living together?' she said at the conclusion of her conversation with her eldest daughter. 'What do you feel about that? Of course, I have no intention of marrying again', she added quickly, sure at that moment this was how she felt. Her daughter's cheerful and sensible attitude to this, as she imagined, startling confession, comforted Elizabeth immensely, especially the final remark before the phone went down: 'and about time too!' which made them both laugh.

The next few weeks approaching Christmas were silent days for Elizabeth; no letter from Michael awaited her amongst her morning's mail, no telephone calls, but being a sensible woman, she reasoned that he had said he was very busy with his photography and could even be away on some assignment. This practical reasoning was called even more into play as the week before Christmas approached. Feeling that a promise had been made when they first met on the train, she would find an attractive Christmas card, and simply send her love signing herself as usual 'Elizabeth'. This use of her full name was because she had told him how she loved the way he said it; it was their private shared thought. In fact, she very rarely used her full name except with those met on first acquaintance. To her also he was always Michael, but phrases such as 'dear man' and 'dear person' had naturally crept into her letters and conversations with him over the past weeks.

It was two days before Christmas when Elizabeth was extremely busy with her preparations for a house full of guests over the festive season, when a card arrived. It was simply signed 'Michael' with the briefest of footnotes thanking her for the card sent from Bruges and without his promised holiday photographs. As soon as she opened the card, Elizabeth received what she could only describe to herself as a blow under the rib cage. At times she almost doubled over with pain which remained with her day and night throughout the week of Christmas and New Year. How she would be able to get through all the entertaining and work of providing a happy time for those about her she would never know; her thoughts by now were so entirely focused on Michael.

The extraordinary thing to her on looking back to this period was the fact she never connected this pain with any incipient illness of her own, and had formulated the opinion that she was 'receiving' the pain from somewhere else, but had no idea from where it came. Elizabeth had never experienced anything of this nature before in her normally very healthy body, and not having any time at all to explore the reasons for such unwanted physical symptoms, she did not analyse what was happening to her.

The dull cold days of January followed and still Elizabeth was in pain, at times quite severe, and for a reason she never could explain then or later, she still made no appointment to see a doctor. Her distress at this time was compounded as she had received absolutely no communication of any sort from Michael during these long weeks.

In her physical and mental distress, Elizabeth finally took into her confidence a close friend, a very wise woman who listened to all she had to say making no comment as the tale unfolded from beginning to end. Elizabeth told her of the unusual meeting with her friend from the train, their letters and extended talks over the telephone at night, and then the total silence that had followed now for many weeks. Elizabeth finally confessed her visit to the palmist in the early days of her acquaintance with Michael, feeling rather foolish in admitting her weakness at the time.

To her surprise her friend Diana took it all very calmly, and being asked for her advice, said she was of the opinion that Elizabeth and Michael were destined to meet, and in light of all that had gone before it would be quite in order to write a simple letter thanking him for his Christmas card and await events.

After this comforting talk with her friend, Elizabeth began to feel that she had a certain role in Michael's life, but what that role was she had no idea at all. Many times she thought of telephoning him, but in the absence of any replies to her letters she felt unable to intrude further into his life. His earlier reference to her 'sweet letters' and his encouragement to keep writing had kept her holding on to this small thread of comfort, a thread she knew with some inner certainty was there and which bound them together.

By the end of January Elizabeth was gradually coming to the conclusion that she had entirely misinterpreted the situation between herself and the briefly met stranger of the year before. After all, she reasoned with herself, it had been a very long time since she had been emotionally involved with anyone in any way; she envied to a degree the open honesty of the present generation, particularly the young women of her granddaughter's age who seemed to be able to manage these things far more easily. However, she would not be prepared to emulate, in her view, the extremes of throwing themselves into intimate associations without real love and friendship being first solidly established between the partners of their choice.

At this time Elizabeth felt a child in her emotions; nothing previously experienced had prepared her for the events of the past few months. There was not the slightest doubt of her love for the character of the man she had met – as she had told her young friend some time ago, it was the mind that had proved the attraction and not the body. She reviewed his qualities, his straightforward way of dealing with things, with no prevarication on any subject, and if he did not want to discuss a certain point then his 'No' meant exactly that. This 'No' at times had made Elizabeth laugh, it was so very direct and caused her not the slightest offence, although the negative when she had tentatively suggested a meeting some time had certainly surprised her. Now this negative assumed more of an importance in her mind than perhaps it should have in light of his total silence of many weeks.

The telephone when it rang with loud insistence found her sitting on her sofa, and she reached out to pick it up expecting one of her family to be ringing for an early evening chat. To her surprise she heard that pleasant, now familiar voice, saying without any preamble, but with some urgent insistence, 'Grab a pen and write this down'.

'Where are you?' she tried to say as she fumbled quickly for a pen and notepad, a thousand questions in her mind, but without answering her half spoken questions he repeated his words and Elizabeth did as instructed, her mind buzzing with joy to hear his voice, but totally mystified at this novel start to their usual conversations.

'Listen, get this down – I am in hospital, it is no good you writing letters to my home address, I am giving you the address of a good friend of mine who has promised to bring my mail in for me when visiting'.

With questions tumbling off her lips in quick succession she asked, 'What happened? Why are you there? How long have you been there?'

He quietly stemmed the flow of her words by explaining that in December he had begun to feel unwell, his skin going very yellow, so had made an appointment to see the doctor for a check-up. After all the tests they told him their diagnosis.

'I am dying, I have cancer of the pancreas,' he concluded.

The shock of the news left Elizabeth's face drained of colour, and she was glad she was sitting down. She immediately rallied, and without a thought for her normal female reticence she called him "Darling" and knew that now all her efforts should be in giving him her total love and support in this terrible blow to all the hopes and dreams of a few happy weeks of the previous year.

Michael went on to tell her that he had been in hospital for six weeks after his operation and would soon be going to recuperate in a nursing home, hopefully one near his home. At present he did not know which place he would be sent to, and this was the reason why he was asking her to write via his friend. She promised to write every week on a Monday so he would know when to expect her letters.

When this short conversation was over Elizabeth broke down and wept, the strain of the past weeks now culminating in this terrible news. In this state of shock her mind flew from the happy thought that he had at last renewed contact with her; their possible life together seemed in ruins at her feet, and she wept again, unable to stop the tears running down her face.

Next morning, distressed beyond measure, Elizabeth rushed up to see her friend Diana who, apart from being a close friend, had also in recent years lost a very dear daughter from cancer, and she knew she could rely on her understanding.

Making some large mugs of coffee, Diana carried them through to where they sat and patiently waited whilst her evidently very distressed friend unburdened herself of her sorrow and fears for the life of her now, she had to acknowledge, most precious friend. As expected, Diana was most supportive, offering practical advice on the importance of love and understanding for the patient suffering from cancer, stressing the need to act normally as far as possible, leaving the reins of control still firmly held in their own hands. She recommended certain books on the subject which would be helpful, and finally allowing her friend to leave with a little ray of hope that remissions have occurred, and one could never dismiss the possibility of a miracle.

It just happened that Elizabeth had reason to go and visit her own doctor that week on a routine matter, and as she always felt at ease with him, asked if he would give her a few minutes of his time to give her a prognosis of someone with cancer of the pancreas. She told him that her friend had been fitted with a shunt at the time of the operation. The doctor sat back in his swivel chair, and looking her frankly in the face, told her that it was difficult for him to comment as he did not have the facts before him, and obviously did not know the patient in question. Elizabeth however, pressed him for the probable prognosis for someone in the situation she had outlined to him, and he told her that her friend could have up to three months to live, although in very rare cases patients had lived up to a year. She thanked him with all her usual courtesy, numbed with the facts of the case so clearly and unemotionally outlined for her.

At this moment, as these realities started to sink in, Elizabeth felt ready to storm Heaven's gate to relieve her friend from the fate that seemed to be in store for him. How could their nascent love, arriving so late in their joint lives, be allowed to die almost as soon as it was born? Surely love could conquer all; maybe if she was able to look after him and make him happy, this might produce a chemical change in him, which would repel the deadly invader of his body. With these very slender threads of hope she poured out her love to him in her next letter, sending him a photograph of herself when twenty-one, beautifully dressed in a white evening dress, her black hair gleaming above her slim bare shoulders. As usual she interspersed her letter with jokes and narrative passages describing the beauties of the countryside surrounding her home.

Michael's next letter was very brief as he was still not strong, and he then went on to warn her, 'There are certain things between us better unsaid just now, there's no need, our wavebands are the same so I understand.' He told her he especially liked her photograph. For the first time he went on to share with her his innermost thoughts, and described how he had lain awake at night unable to sleep thinking of past joys and happiness, his love for the English countryside and his music. He followed by thoughts of being devoured by the monster inside of him – writing 'How does mind conquer this?... God?' He then wrote that a priest came into the ward that day and sat beside his bed. Michael showed him these night thoughts which he had illustrated by a little sketch on a piece of paper.

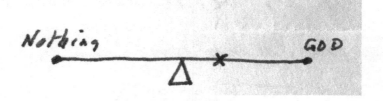

He told her that the priest was mute for several minutes, and then asked, 'Why did you draw the second question mark?' Michael then explained to him why he had drawn the sketch of a balance, explaining he had, as he put it in his letter to Elizabeth, 'Settled for the 'X' to dispel that awful low of "Nothing". To Elizabeth's joy he concluded his letter by saying, 'I feel the sunny warmth of your friendship. I'm positive again,' signing himself as before, 'Love, Michael.'

It was this letter that was to have great importance to them both in times to come.

Chapter IX

Forte

It was from this time that Elizabeth was trying in her letters to turn Michael's thoughts from disease and death. Because of his confidences she felt able to open up her own heart more fully and share with him some of her own inner self and the beautiful place – the plateau she retired to in her thoughts and dreams when life became particularly difficult.

'I am for short or long periods on a beautiful plateau with grassy fields, swathes of flowers of every hue as far as the eye can see, whispering grasses with occasional glimpses of water between low hills, glorious sunlight, sparkling air and then up again off a rocky path clinging at times on to shifting ledges on my way up, however knowing I shall make it, poor fool I am, if I just keep going. Meeting you, dear man, is one of those grassy plains full of sunlight and tiny rivulets of water sparkling in the light, sending off shards of light like a diamond – on the edges of these tiny life-giving streams of water are minute ferns tucked between the stones. Birds fill the flowering shrubs and trees lifting their throats in a cascade of sound.'

The rapport this exploration of their most intimate thoughts had led Elizabeth to decide that if Michael would agree, she would make every effort to go up to London to see if her cheerful company would help him in his recuperation. With positive thoughts of this nature she waited patiently for news of his move to the nursing home, and perhaps finally his agreement that he would at least permit her to see him once again. She had scrupulously avoided raising this with him either in conversation or in her letters, feeling that his wishes should be respected, particularly on this point.

The following week, a long envelope with Michael's own familiar hand-writing arrived, and with eager fingers she ripped the envelope open preparing to read his letter with enjoyment as she ate her breakfast. His opening words told of his removal to the expected nursing home giving her the address and his telephone number. The next paragraph she read over and over again with great shock.

'I want to be entirely honest with you so there are no misunderstandings between us,' and then went on to explain that years ago he had been, as he put it, intimately associated with a girlfriend whom he had hoped would come to live permanently with him, but things had not worked out for them for various reasons. (These reasons he had briefly touched on in their first conversation on the train). Elizabeth read on with a growing sense of unhappiness, 'And now, due to my present illness, this has triggered a compassionate response in her, and so I'm sure you understand the emotional turmoil I'm feeling when I read your letters and that is why, in my last letter, I asked you to leave sentiment between us unsaid for the present.'

Hardly daring to read the remaining paragraph which Elizabeth feared contained words of a final break between them, she allowed her eyes to encompass his comforting words as he continued to write in his usual refrain.

What an enchanting pastoral scene you painted for me in your last letter! It was both an escape and comfort to me. If my music recovers sufficiently again, I feel I could set your scene to music.' Quoting her phrase about life-giving streams he added his own word pictures to hers – 'Contrasting with these tiny green ferns I see also butterflies flitting between purple and white foxgloves which swing like slender sentinels of tranquillity,' signing himself at the end of the letter, 'With love Michael.'

Elizabeth put the letter down and not for the first time felt that she was getting conflicting signals from her friend who was becoming increasingly dear to her as the weeks passed by. His words referring to his emotional turmoil affected her greatly, and she felt extremely unhappy that she should, however inadvertently, have given pain to someone recovering from such a serious illness. She felt that she had unconsciously entered an emotional minefield and was standing in the centre, stunned to find herself in this situation.

After some quiet reflection to allow herself time to recover and get a balanced view of where she thought she stood with Michael, Elizabeth made a decision that in fact this earlier love did not change things; he was above all her friend. Her inner certainty which rarely left her, although seriously wavering on receipt of his words, reasserted itself with the recognition of her role as comforter and friend. For some reason she knew that he had some need of her friendship and, being realistic, was also aware of the same need of his old friends, which included, she sensibly concluded, old girlfriends.

This finally achieved resolution of their situation allowed her to write in response to his letter that she was, 'grieved to have caused him this inner turmoil' he spoke of, adding she quite understood how he felt at this time, concluding with an apology for her, as she put it, 'crass behaviour which had given him pain'.

The remainder of her letter was filled with cheerful and she hoped entertaining stories, keeping any emotional content strictly under control as he wished. Feeling she had done all she could to get their relationship back on an even keel once more she, with some trepidation, posted off her letter.

The following days went by on leaden feet as Elizabeth endeavoured to keep herself busy with anything that involved the maximum amount of physical work, allowing her to drop into bed each night exhausted with her labours. Most of these labours were directed to her garden, where as she had told Michael, she drew so much spiritual strength, and where now she was able to gain some sort of peace from her troubled thoughts.

Despite all her attempts to suppress thoughts of Michael, her mind continued in its by now accustomed way, storing items to write and tell him about when she next corresponded. The tiny candle of hope lit in her mind had not gone out; she felt she still had some sort of role in his life, a role yet to be defined. If that role was to be as comforter and friend, she could manage that. Nevertheless, there was another thread of thought running through her mind, which in fact probably had developed from the day of their original meeting, that there was a special purpose to their first encounter over and above the role of friend. It was during this period she felt that her whole being was tuned into his; all her will, her thoughts, were directed towards him. Each day she felt the need, as she put it to herself, to be with Michael. This meant a need to be alone, almost as if by tuning in to his thoughts and emotions with no outside interruptions this would enable her to keep writing each week. She instinctively seemed to be responding to some unuttered conversation which was taking place between them. She explored his needs, his anxieties, with no word said between them. This fine thread of silent communication was with her all her waking hours. She could be doing her shopping, and as she walked around the shops, whole pages of thought would be forming in her mind – thoughts she would rush home to place on paper to be incorporated into her next Monday letter. At no time did she feel herself unable to find subjects to talk about to entertain or interest him. At first she wrote about her home, then extended her word pictures as she, 'took him by the hand' as she said in the introduction to these letters, and in her mind's eye take him onto the cliffs, into the woods and surveyed the seascape around her home. These descriptive passages were interwoven with stories of her own and her children's childhoods spent in her beloved Cornwall.

These letters were to her a joy, her gift of love to her friend. Whenever possible she would illustrate them with picture postcards and enjoyed searching for just the right picture to accompany the topic of the week. Without at first recognising the fact, she gradually became aware that she was at the same time showing him aspects of her own self, her history, her thoughts and feelings. These letters were also helping her through this difficult time, giving her the feeling that they were continually in touch. Although rather one-sided, this did not seem to matter to her at all. In fact this uninterrupted communication seemed the most important factor in their relationship at this time, and even Michael's most recent letter with its shock and initial hurt to her feelings, did not destroy it. It was becoming evident that this shared love, reined in by Michael in his impossible situation, was not of a physical nature – she was not 'in love' with Michael, but she loved him to the exclusion of all other previous loves. She knew that the pain she had experienced from the Christmas period indicated how very close they were in spirit right from the start. With his convalescence this pain had gradually lessened, for which she was immensely grateful, grateful that he had benefited from life-saving surgery and was improving in strength daily. Now she felt better able to cope with the problem that had arisen in their relationship.

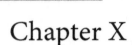

Chapter X

Fortissimo

After what seemed like several very long days to Elizabeth, his letter arrived. It opened with the words, 'My Dear Elizabeth', and asked her not to feel he had been caused any pain or distress.

'You haven't; the seed of friendship planted from our first meeting is flourishing. Perhaps my phrase, I think it was "emotional turmoil" was on reflection rather strong, so let's leave it there. We now understand each other and our friendship remains fully intact.'

He went on to explain exactly where his nursing home was situated in relation to the centre of London and told her she would be welcome to visit him if the journey was not too far, concluding this paragraph by giving her the exact details of the bus and underground connections she would need to take for each part of the journey. Joy was now rising in Elizabeth's breast as she read these words, and felt encouraged that all was well between them.

She read his final paragraphs - 'Although feeling stronger I'm only a shadow of my former self, however I'm trying hard to overcome my illness,' concluding, 'Cornwall in the spring surely must have a place in your plateau,' signing off his letter, 'With love Michael.'

After re-reading this letter many times, Elizabeth, overjoyed that their apparent rift had somehow been healed, now turned all her happy thoughts to the possibility of a visit at long last.

In her next Monday letter, she again took up the theme of her 'plateau,' feeling confident that he wanted to hear more of her words on this particular subject.

'Thank you, dear Michael for adding to my beautiful plateau with your purple and white foxgloves with their attendant butterflies which "gently sway like slender sentinels of tranquillity" and I have placed them, with your permission, in the following part of my special place...' With a smile on her lips and glancing out of the window to her garden for occasional inspiration, she wrote:

'Now I would like to invite you to see the pool which lies below the bank where your sentient foxgloves grow. The edge of the pool is clothed in reeds from which the small black moorhens venture in and out, only to disappear from sight once again. Trout rise to snatch the insects off the shining waters, leaving only a widening ring to show where they have been. The gentle extended ripples reach the golden March Marigolds growing in the sides of the bank, and above dainty Demoiselle dragonflies with gaudy iridescent wings hover and swoop in seemingly perpetual motion. The high cumulus clouds passing above cause shifts of light and colour in the untroubled waters below. The faintest breath of air gently stirs the reeds and their susurrus drowns the senses in dreamy sleep. How lovely to sit beside these waters and dip the tips of one's fingers into their fresh coolness and dream the hours away.'

* * *

It was fortunate that weekend that Elizabeth's eldest son had telephoned indicating he would be coming for a short visit the following week, and agreed that he would be happy to drive his mother either part or all of the way to London on his return home so she could visit Michael.

Before this visit took place, Michael rang one evening and seemed rather embarrassed as he tentatively said, 'I do not know how to put this,' and then, still hesitantly, started to suggest that she might like to meet him somewhere halfway in a few weeks' time.

He went on to say he hoped she would not think it audacious to suggest a meeting, but before he had actually got the words out of his mouth, she said, 'I am coming soon, the next weekend in fact, if that is alright?' and hardly allowing Michael to catch his breath, explained that she would be able to get a lift with her son, and it was too good an opportunity to miss. Both calming down at this point she asked if he knew of a suitable hotel near Waterloo Station where she could book a room, but Michael was not at all happy with this idea and said he would see what he could do to find somewhere nearer the nursing home where he was staying.

'How long can you stay?' he asked.

'Two or three days if you felt up to it'.

He thought it was hardly worth travelling so far for so short a time but Elizabeth assured him it would be worth it to her.

'I am coming up to soothe your fevered brow,' she joked,

'Oh! In that case you must come,' he laughed.

'Where are you phoning from?' she enquired.

'From home, I am sitting in the dark as all the electricity has been switched off.'

'Don't get cold,' she warned. 'Already she is sounding like my mother!' he complained as Elizabeth laughed happily. All their easy companionable talk flowed as usual and, with promises to leave all arrangements at his end to him, his final word 'Dearest' as he put the receiver down left her in an euphoria of happiness.

It was with the happiest of thoughts her hours were now occupied, with questions like, 'What shall I wear?' followed by the more worrying questions, 'Will he like me when he sees me?' 'Suppose he is disappointed with me?' 'Supposing he takes one look and goes away or does not even turn up?' and finally, 'I do hope he is not younger than I am!' All the thoughts of a teenager in love, she chided herself, but now faced with the imminent visit, to finally at last to see the man she had learned to love at a distance, she could not keep these trivial thoughts from entering her mind.

By prior arrangement Elizabeth had a chance to visit Exeter a few days before her proposed visit to London, and taking the opportunity of a lift from a friend, employed her time with various business appointments and a little shopping. One item on her list was as a suitable gift to give Michael on her impending visit. He had said not to bring food; he was sick of it, nevertheless she finally decided that a few well chosen, delicious handmade chocolates might be rather categorised as a treat than a food, and so made her modest purchase, feeling she had solved this small problem satisfactorily. She had arranged to meet her friend for lunch, but having completed all her shopping, she still had a half hour to spare. With her mind never really leaving the man who occupied her emotions, hopes and fears, her feet naturally led her to the cathedral. On her enquiry at the door for a place of private prayer, the custodian directed her to the Lady Chapel.

On her entry Elizabeth saw the chapel was empty, peaceful and quiet, and she knelt in prayer for some time asking the aid of heaven for her friend in need. After a while she sat up contemplating her surroundings and allowed the natural tears to fall in a silent stream down her face. The relief of placing the life of her loved one into higher hands was enormous, and feeling much calmer, she left the chapel. At the entrance she noted a board, unperceived on her entry, which had been placed for the writing of the names of those for whom special prayers were sought. Elizabeth wrote Michael's name down, and her sense of humour never far from the surface, had to smile at the either Japanese or Chinese characters written by some foreign visitor to the chapel, and just hoped the Bishop was able to read this unusually inscribed request.

Feeling cheered with the renewed hope that miracles did happen, and in the knowledge she had done everything she could from a distance to help Michael in his present ordeal, she went off light-heartedly for her lunch.

Chapter XI

Harmony

By the time her son had arrived for his visit the following week, Elizabeth was in a state of nervous apprehension. A day or two before, Michael had telephoned to say he had arranged for her to stay with friends of his, near neighbours who could put her up for one night only. Michael told her that he had also organised dinner for them so they could spend the evening together. His next surprising news was that another friend had offered to drive him up to Waterloo Station, and he would meet her there himself.

'Supposing my train is delayed or I miss it?' queried Elizabeth.

Michael assured her that he would sit and wait for two consecutive trains so as not to miss her. She had demurred at the thought of him waiting for her in the cold, afraid he was not strong enough to be travelling all over London to meet her, but he assured her that he would come to no harm at all just sitting and waiting. Elizabeth was astonished that he was proposing all this in the light of his having so recently left hospital, but the only direct reference he made to his illness was a proviso that should he have a relapse whilst they were out of direct contact he would give her his friend's telephone number who would be able to give her any up-to-date news. He anxiously asked her the size of the overnight bag she would be carrying, and they had an enjoyable few minutes whilst he enquired about the exact contents. With his persuasion she revealed the contents of a lady's overnight bag item by item; he must be feeling better, she thought, but it was only after the phone went down she realised his real concern was that he would not be able to carry it for her.

How will we recognise each other? – was another theme of their conversation.

'I will recognise you, you are unforgettable,' he said firmly, adding, 'Do not worry, I will see to everything.' She made him laugh by saying she had lain awake thinking will it be a 'Dr Livingstone, I presume' type of meeting with formal handshakes.

'I would hate to kiss the wrong man on the cheek!' she said laughingly.

'Do not worry,' was his reply, 'I will take care of everything.' Their final arrangement was for the exact place of their rendezvous at the station.

'I will meet you on the balcony above the departure point for the Eurostar trains,' a description completely baffling to Elizabeth who had not been to Waterloo station for some years, and certainly not since the inception of the Channel Tunnel.

'I am only a country girl,' she remarked, explaining her lack of knowledge in this direction.

Michael then gave her explicit directions, which she jotted down in her diary: 'Turn left immediately you leave the exit gate from your arrival platform and continue on down the concourse until you come to the balcony; I will be waiting for you there – you cannot miss it,' he added; she hoped he was right. As Elizabeth finally put the telephone down she felt sure that he would, as he said, take care of everything, and luxuriated in this thought.

Now careful, but pleasurable preparations went ahead for this all so important meeting and all the happiness implied by thoughts of seeing each other again. Elizabeth indulged in the purchase of some light scent, she instinctively felt he would not like anything heavy or extravagant, and a pair of fine stockings before packing her bag for the few days away. If things turned out well on this visit, she intended booking into a hotel for a further one or two nights, but would leave her options open. Before embarking on her journey, she also decided she could always catch a return train home if they hated each other on sight. I hope I am not making the biggest mistake of my life, was her last thought as she drifted off to sleep that night.

Because of Michael's unexpected arrangements to meet Elizabeth in person at Waterloo, it was decided that her son would drive her part of the way on his own journey to London, and then put her on a train halfway so she would arrive at the correct time and place without disturbing Michael's plans.

By the time they had driven up to the station the following day Elizabeth was very nervous, and almost anything at this point would have made her turn around and go home, but her son grabbed her case and efficiently conducted her to the carriage door of her train.

'Good luck,' he said giving her a big hug and pushed her in, giving her little time for a last-minute attack of stage fright.

'It's a great adventure,' she told him as they waved each other goodbye.

Confident she had done all she could to look her best, Elizabeth relaxed in her seat and allowed her mind to drift back to that other train journey which had changed her life so dramatically. On reflection, they had seemed to be suspended from reality on that whole journey, and now the fact that she was going to meet someone she had briefly met only once had not escaped her, adding to the dream-like nature of their encounter. Her main thought was for Michael's welfare, whether he was strong enough to be embarking on this adventure of theirs, or if he in fact had already had the relapse, he had warned her might happen at any time. The very tenuous nature of the whole meeting was riven with this and other worries, the last of which was would they end up missing each other and be destined finally never to meet again?

The train pulled up only five minutes late at Waterloo Station, and Elizabeth smartly descended from the train, and walked up the long platform towards the gate. Michael had told her to turn left directly she came out of the gate and she would then find his balcony, the place of their intended rendezvous, a little way further along in the same direction.

There was quite a small crowd standing around the gate as she and the other passengers attempted to go their separate ways. Above the crowd to the right Elizabeth glimpsed a tall man standing at the back, remarking to herself on his height, but mindful of Michael's instructions and realising her train was a little late, hastened to the meeting place.

Having arrived at the balcony, she stood with her bag on the ground beside her, and looked around. She looked up and down the platform amongst the busy crowd with no sign of anyone apparently looking for her. She had a sudden lapse of memory and could not remember if he had said below or above the balcony, and so travelled down the short escalator to the entrance to the Eurostar trains. There were very few people here, and certainly no one bearing the faintest resemblance to the man she had come to meet, and so she returned to her original place above.

A few minutes passed and Elizabeth realised in this crowd

she would have to identify Michael for herself, as apparently, he was nowhere to be seen. The only clue he had given her on the telephone when they had mutually agreed it did not matter how each other looked, it was not important, he had added he always carried his camera with him in a bag slung across his shoulders. With this sole clue in mind, Elizabeth anxiously scrutinised each person around her carefully, and then saw a tall figure approaching her, rather yellow in the face due to his illness she surmised, with an old bag slung over his shoulder.

Some glimmer of that profile seen last year in the train made her say tentatively as he approached, 'Michael?' simultaneously with his 'Elizabeth' as he rushed towards her in relief and gathered her into a bear hug, kissing her on the cheek as he did so.

'I couldn't find you,' she gasped in relief.

'Where were you?' he replied and went on to explain, 'I waited by your gate to give you a surprise!' and they both laughed, she remembering the tall man glimpsed at the back of the crowd as she first came out of her gate. Her happiness spilled out, and in the most natural way possible held his hand, her small one in the firm grasp of his large one, and tried to keep up with his long stride. She had insisted on carrying her own bag as she felt he should not be obliged to lift heavy objects, and he sensibly allowed her to do so without any argument.

'It all comes flooding back,' he remarked as hand in hand they walked out of the station. Talking all the way, as usual, they covered a diverse range of subjects in the first few minutes of meeting. He proposed they should go to the Royal Festival Hall and have a warm drink, and as Elizabeth had been up early that morning she gladly agreed. As they approached the Festival Hall Elizabeth told him how she and her husband, then newly married, had been to concerts at the Hall all those years ago; it must have been newly built then, she added.

They seemed to fly along the pavements, Elizabeth feeling that at any moment she and her bag might take off as she attempted to keep up with his quick strides, and soon arrived at the Hall. She was surprised and pleased with Michael's vigour, and apart from the yellow tinge to his skin, felt it would be difficult to see that he was suffering from a terminal illness.

In the atrium upstairs a group of singers were singing plainsong to the customers enjoying their refreshments, but to Elizabeth's amusement Michael turned his nose up at this particular type of music, which she found to be a pleasant accompaniment to their proposed meal. Michael insisted on queuing himself for bowls of soup and tea while Elizabeth sat and rested, watching his tall, slim figure patiently standing on the other side of the spacious interior. All her nervous worries had evaporated and she was prepared to enjoy to the full their short time together.

Elizabeth had to admit that now she had again met Michael, the impact on her of his physical presence was very strong. It had nothing to do with his actual appearance, he was not handsome in the normally accepted way, but there was something in him which drew her to him with feelings first noticed at their original meeting.

Bearing two large, colourful bowls of soup and some tea on a tray, he placed this on the table she had chosen and both tucked in, enjoying the companionship of the meal together. He had also purchased an apple and meticulously cut this into quarters offering her a piece which she accepted with pleasure. He told her he was always hungry after his operation, but as he was unused to large meals, he suffered quite frequently from stomach pains. Elizabeth, assuming her motherly role for a minute advised 'little and often' as a good guide to ease the problem.

After their bowls of soup had been eaten, they sat back and looked at each other.

'You are smaller than I remember,' he told her.

'And you are taller,' Elizabeth returned, 'I supposed you were jack-knifed into your seat on the train.'

'You really are the country girl you said you were in your letters. When I met you on the train, I thought you were a sophisticated woman with lots of make-up,' he added as an afterthought. Elizabeth had to repress a smile at this interpretation of her appearance as 'sophisticated' but made no comment.

Michael outlined the rest of the day's programme and enquired if she had taken his advice about a gift for her host and hostess for the night, a box of tea bags. She laughingly explained she had brought a large box and this was filling up half her overnight bag. He thoroughly approved of her choice, and having finished their lunch they returned to the station, this time to go below to the Underground to catch their train, which would take them to the outskirts of the city.

Elizabeth was rather nonplussed as to how she was to get herself, together with both her hand and overnight bags, on to the fast-moving escalator, but Michael relieved her of her handbag which was threatening to slide down her arm and entangle itself in her feet. He then took her arm in a surprisingly strong grip and so they descended the long steep stairs with no mishap at either end.

It had been some years since Elizabeth had been on the London Underground railway and she was surprised to see how much lighter and cleaner it appeared. She was glad to have Michael with her as he seemed to know exactly which train to board, and finding a seat easily at that time of day, they sat together for the three-quarter hour journey. Mindful that Michael had said this was his first trip out from the nursing home, she sat quietly at his side and hoped he would take the opportunity to rest a little. Elizabeth had plenty to think about, one thought remaining in her mind above all others, was that she found it difficult to believe that here she actually was with this person who had become so important to her. She was surprised too how well he seemed to be coping with his day, and thought he was far better than she could possibly have imagined. He had told her on the telephone that the surgeons had not been able to remove all of the growth on his pancreas, and she was worried by the colour of his skin which evidently showed that all was not well with him despite his energetic manner. She must have voiced these thoughts at some time during their conversation as he told her he had always been fit and wiry. Judging by his grip on her arm and his strength of grasp on her hand she could see that he was not wrong.

During their journey Michael confided to her in his usual open way that because he had never married some people thought he was homosexual. Elizabeth, giving him a merry glance said, 'I certainly don't think that!' and he smiled, adding, 'I think I must be a loner really'. Endearingly, he had told her when he first met her, he had, as he put it, 'all his working parts', but now was a shadow of himself. Elizabeth renewed her grip on his hand as they both relapsed into silence, sitting as she reflected, looking rather like Darby and Joan to anyone interested enough to notice them.

At journey's end there was a quick walk for a bus to take them to their final destination. Then they walked from the bus station and approached the nursing home, which on entering Elizabeth found was more like a luxurious hotel, beautifully appointed and furnished.

Upon arrival Michael took her up in the lift, at the same time exchanging pleasantries with some of the other guests staying there, none of whom looked either ill or infirm, Elizabeth reflected as Michael led her to his room to leave her overnight bag.

His room was attractively furnished with antique pieces and had a pleasant outlook onto a large expanse of carefully mown lawns with large mature trees at the far end. They both availed themselves of the opportunity to have a wash, and leaving Elizabeth's overnight bag there as planned for the time being, went off in search of a possible cup of tea.

Early afternoon tea at a little table in the drawing room was just over, but Michael managed to persuade one of the waitresses to bring in a tray for them as they were both very thirsty from travelling. As before at lunch when they had portioned the apple between them, they shared the one portion of the cake left for them, perfectly happy in each other's company. Their seat on the sofa was beside an upright piano, and Michael promised Elizabeth that he would play for her some of his own compositions after dinner. Elizabeth looked forward with great pleasure to this delightful programme arranged for her.

On their return to his room after tea Elizabeth realised that Michael should have a rest and indicated she had brought a book with her, and was therefore quite happy to put her feet up in the large wing chair by the window while he rested between tea and supper. He told her he did not want to rest, and they both agreed the rather clinical looking bed with its crackling white duvet did not look too inviting.

Elizabeth fished into her overnight bag and produced her small gift of hand-made chocolates. Michael seemed delighted with this little present and insisted on sharing them with her right away.

'I want to see you enjoy that,' he said standing right in front of her as he watched her slowly taking bites from a large of chocolate, he had urged her to take from the cellophane wrapping. Watched intently by Michael and feeling rather like a bird being fed with titbits, Elizabeth had no difficulty in giving him signs of her pleasure. Without much urging he joined her for their treat.

'I will keep the rest for us to enjoy after dinner'. 'But I brought them all for *you* to enjoy', she protested, knowing from his actions that her protests would not be listened to on this point.

Finding the room warm, Elizabeth took off her jacket and small Elizabethan-style velvet hat, preparing to drop them over the back of a chair, but Michael took them from her and, placing the cap on his own head, capered across the room, making imaginary sword play as he went. Elizabeth watched him with indulgent motherly feelings, glad he was able to act so naturally in her presence.

'It ought to have a feather in it,' he remarked as he took it off and placed it beside the jacket on the bed.

'Yes, well... it did once, but a child riding by on his father's shoulders in the centre of town snatched it out before I realised what had happened, and disappeared from my sight in the crowded street before I could retrieve it!'

They laughed, and abandoning his sword play Michael insisted that Elizabeth take the only comfortable chair in the room, telling her she should relax there. He then crossed the room, and decisively picked up the only other seat, a straight-backed bedroom chair, turning it around and sat astride with the words, 'Let's talk what do you want to know?'

As her feet were feeling tired, Elizabeth asked if he would mind if she slipped off her shoes, and without a word he went to a cupboard full of old shoes and produced an enormous (to her eyes) pair of well-worn slippers. She slipped them on, exclaiming how they hung down several inches below her own heels, but glad of their comfort and ease. His natural behaviour further endeared him to her, and she felt not the slightest strain in this one-to-one situation.

As on all those other times, their conversation ranged over a very large number of subjects. First, he told her all about his operation and the unpleasant effects of the surgeon's first attempts to tackle the tumour from above, and not being successful had to then approach the pancreas from below. Because of the delicate nature of this procedure, sited so close to other important organs, he had to stay awake for the duration to enable him to tell the surgeons how he was feeling as the operation progressed, adding this was not a pleasant experience for him. She remembered he had told her in their earlier telephone conversation from the hospital how to his surprise his thoughts during the operation had drifted to visions of fields, flowers and the lovely peaceful ways of the country. He then went on to tell her that there was still a part of the growth left behind which, due to its situation, they had not been able to reach. Elizabeth had been given to understand from her visit to her own doctor the dangers and difficulties of operating in this area so close to other vital organs, but was puzzled that he did not seem to be receiving some kind of chemotherapy or other treatment to deal with the remainder of the tumour left behind. Reminded by this topic, Elizabeth delved into her handbag and handed him a newspaper cutting she had seen recently relating to an article about a new advanced treatment that was under trial at that time. He told her he was already aware of this, but made no other comment.

Wishing to divert Michael to other more pleasant subjects, Elizabeth encouraged him to tell her all about his career, and he explained that his earlier profession had been in engineering. He described some of the interesting work he had done which had led him in the last War to a reserved occupation as his work was so important to the War effort. Elizabeth was always interested in the romance of special projects of this nature having been brought up in an environment of a family business of architecture and building. She persuaded him to explain some of his inventions, which he proceeded to do. He was surprised at her grasp of the technicalities involved, admittedly told to her in mainly layman's terms. It was only in his recent years that he had been able to do anything about his first love of music and how ended up teaching this in a well-known College of Music.

He broke off and looking at her said, 'You are so understanding and interested in so many subjects; I noticed this when we were talking on the train.' Elizabeth smiled at this compliment, glad that he was so happily engaged in reliving the past.

He then went on to discuss some of her writings which she had earlier sent him to look over for her. He said her handwritten loops and curlicues were very feminine, but at first, he had found it rather hard to read. Upon hearing this criticism, one made to her frequently by her own family, she promised to try to improve her legibility for him.

'I can always type my letters,' she offered, but he said briefly, 'Don't.'

She then went on to explain that at times the words came tumbling out, and she did not have time to worry about how the writing looked as she could always tidy everything up later.

He nodded, 'The same method as Beethoven who worked on the same principal, get it all down and sort it out later.'

Elizabeth was immensely flattered to be compared in any way to the great composer.

Over an hour went by in absorbing conversation, and finally in a pause, she leant her head back against the chair feeling for an instant very tired, a nerve flicking in her neck.

Michael said, 'Now we have run out of conversation,' but Elizabeth knew that for the present she had run out of strength, and would have been glad to sit quietly in the now fading light.

Michael got up from the chair where he had remained astride as they talked and crossed the room, bending down to kiss her on the lips. Elizabeth was very surprised and got up.

'That was a surprise, wasn't it?' he said.

'Yes', she replied slowly, 'yes it was.'

A moment later they were in each other's arms exchanging passionate kisses. Elizabeth felt her limbs dissolving as if she was going to melt into the floor, such was the intensity of emotion flying between them.

'How cuddly you are,' he remarked as he drew her closer.

Elizabeth smiled. They then stood apart and looked at each other, and she ever mindful of his health, yet still wishing to give him all of the health and strength at her command, ran her hands down his arms and back, soothing and loving him as she would have soothed a wounded or distressed animal or child. There was no sexual content in her seeking to give him comfort and relief from stress, caressing his painfully thin body, ending by stroking his hands and long fingers. Michael stood quietly throughout allowing her to give of herself in the only way possible in their situation. Finally, Elizabeth was content to leave matters there knowing there was more time together, and there would be other times to exchange loving physical gestures.

As the supper at the nursing home was early, they both busied themselves in tidying up, she with her heart overflowing with previously undreamed-of love and happiness. She had told Michael she was surprised that he had kissed her, and that was perfectly true; their relationship until that moment had always been as loving friends. In the light of his serious illness she had never expected it to be anything else and had been until now perfectly content with this; for her to be with him was enough.

In a glow of happiness, they descended to the dining room where the dinner prepared for them was being served. How proud Elizabeth felt entering the room at the side of this, in her eyes, lovely man; she felt everyone could see the glow of happiness in her every movement and gesture.

By now, Elizabeth rather hungry, enjoyed her meal and amused herself listening to Michael's potted history of the other guests at the home. He seemed to find congenial company there and they had all enjoyed his playing the piano for them upon occasion.

After dinner Michael went to collect his music leaving Elizabeth in the drawing room where they had enjoyed their coffee. On his return he sat down at the piano, but immediately got up again and in a gesture becoming familiar to her, grabbed hold of a nearby low seat and placing it at one end of the piano, gestured her to sit there. Having re-seated himself to his satisfaction and arranging his music, he played one or two familiar pieces, and then embarked on one of his own partly finished compositions. Elizabeth gave herself up to the enchantment of the evening as she watched his clever brown hands draw out the notes with evident enjoyment. At that moment, Elizabeth thought her cup of happiness would overflow, and when he turned from the keyboard looking directly into her eyes telling her the next piece was dedicated to her, she was surprised and pleased. As the well-known piece of music by Mendelssohn was played, tears of happiness escaped from her eyes. As Michael played, he continually turned to look into her eyes, soul meeting soul in their wordless communication. This love she knew they now shared received confirmation at every glance of his luminous brown eyes, so expressive and bright.

Later, as if in a dream, they collected her overnight bag from his room and made the short bus journey to his friend's house, where Elizabeth was to stay the night. As they sat in the bus, she stroked the back of his long, clever fingers.

'I am purring,' he confided, a remark that made her smile once again, her happiness complete.

It was now quite dark as they got off the bus, and Elizabeth was enchanted by the cherry trees in full bloom, shaped like umbrellas, lining the roads on each side and lit underneath by the street lamps. She tried to linger, but seeing Michael almost disappearing round the next corner unaware that she had stayed behind to enjoy the sight, she ran to catch him up.

As soon as he rang the bell his friends were at the door welcoming them in. They were still at supper, and tired as she was and longing for a bath and bed, she sat at table with her hosts of the night and exchanged pleasantries and news of Michael's progress in the nursing home. Cups of tea were produced whilst their meal was concluded, and Elizabeth found herself relaxing in the company of such a pleasant couple. It was quite evident that the pair of old friends were very fond of Michael who had until only recently been a near neighbour of many years standing. Their generosity in providing a night's lodging for a stranger was proof to her of their affection for him. Elizabeth forgot her tiredness in her enjoyment in seeing another facet of her friend as he laughed and joked with them both.

Eventually Michael said his goodnights, embracing each

of them in turn, and left to return to the nursing home, having arranged to meet her again the next morning at ten o'clock.

After the events of this wonderful day Elizabeth knew that the feelings that had been overwhelming her in the past months had not led her astray.

Chapter XII
Diminuendo

After a welcome hot bath Elizabeth had a long sleep, and next morning enjoyed a protracted breakfast getting to know her hosts. Later, whilst the household was busy with other concerns, she settled in the morning room with a book to await Michael's imminent arrival.

Ten o'clock passed and then eleven; by then Elizabeth had obviously become very agitated, terrified Michael had overdone his first outing, or even possibly suffered a relapse. These fears were not unfounded as he had himself warned her, not long before, when she set out on her journey to meet him, that he could have a relapse at any time. Her hostess, seeing her fears and recognising her very real concerns, which by then were shared by them all, suggested she should telephone the nursing home. Elizabeth felt a little embarrassed that she had so clearly shown her feelings, but due to the kindness shown to her was able to confess that she cared very deeply for Michael.

'Then telephone him,' she was again advised, and without another word, went off to dial the number for her. To Elizabeth's relief she was informed by the nursing home that he had left a short while ago, and so was able to calm herself before his arrival, as she hoped, in the next few minutes.

When Michael arrived fifteen minutes later, he was busy explaining as he entered the house, the confusion of the staff at the home, who had somehow forgotten to bring him his breakfast, and this was the reason why he had left so late. He cheered them all up by saying that he had slept very well for the first time since his operation, which led Elizabeth to think that their happy evening may well have done him some good.

A cup of coffee was suggested, and again they all sat around the table talking of past times, Elizabeth content to listen and join in now and then. A great deal of laughter and affectionate teasing took place, she and Michael behaving like a couple of teenagers.

By then it was nearly lunch time, and after some discussion, they were both pressed to stay for a simple meal of bread and soup. Although Elizabeth was happy to fall in with whatever made Michael happy, she could not stop a little disappointment entering her mind as she had very much hoped that they would have some time to themselves. While lunch was being prepared Michael went into the dining room and played on the piano. Their hosts were delighted with his playing and said how much improved he was in health from a few days previously, and Michael's enjoyment among old friends was Elizabeth's too at that moment.

Nothing in particular had been arranged for their day together; in fact, Elizabeth did not know whether she would be looking for a hotel for the next night or two, or be travelling home that day. She had armed herself with train departure times for the afternoon and evening so as to leave their plans as fluid as possible to suit those of Michael. He had said, 'Leave everything to me,' and with that she was quite content to go at his pace, at the same time not allowing him to tire himself needlessly in providing entertainment for her.

The snack lunch followed in much the same mode as their earlier meals, Elizabeth listening to the details of Michael's life as seen from the perspective of close and affectionate friends. At no time did Elizabeth feel left out of their reminiscences, and very much enjoyed the photographs produced showing Michael in a different light as a much younger man. Michael had a lovely laugh and a great sense of fun. During their affectionate teasing Elizabeth clapped her hand over Michael's mouth to prevent some joking response, he making mouthing noises as if to continue speaking whilst his brown eyes above her hand gleamed in fun. Elizabeth could not help feeling astonished at their ease and familiarity after only a few hours spent together.

Naturally Michael's friends were curious about the relationship between Michael and herself, and he explained they had met on a train, going on to say that Elizabeth was a writer and he had offered to help her in the publication of one of her small technical works. Apparently, their affection for each other did not need any other explanation, their frequent glances at each other and smiles led to their hostess chiding her husband for taking a seat next to Elizabeth.

'Do move, they want to sit together!' she said as she shooed him off to a seat across the room, leaving the two to sit side by side on a small sofa. Being left alone for a minute or two, Elizabeth swiftly kissed Michael on the mouth, much to his apparent delight, before the return of their hostess cut short any further exchanges of love.

It was natural during the conversation between old friends that nearly all those mentioned were unknown to Elizabeth, but the enquiry directed to Michael as to how his old girlfriend was, the one mentioned to Elizabeth in Michael's not to be forgotten letter to her from hospital, caused her a momentary pang.

However, after Michael's few naturally spoken words of reply, with no apparent undertones, Elizabeth was left realising that she should not overreact to a perfectly normal part of the ongoing conversation. Neither then, nor later that day did Michael make any allusion whatever to this other presence in his life.

By the time lunch had been cleared away Elizabeth had begun to wonder if she should broach the subject of the exact time of her departure, but it soon became apparent that Michael had definite arrangements that day with relatives arriving to see him, relations from abroad. This situation had been touched on by Michael in one of their last telephone conversations before meeting, and although he had delayed their arrival in order to fit in her visit, it now appeared that they would be with him early that evening and not in a few days' time as she had expected.

Two factors were now in the background of Elizabeth's mind, one was the need not to overtire Michael, and although he had indicated he wished she would stay another night, Elizabeth realised she would only get in the way of this family reunion, a reunion she suspected in her heart of hearts was to say their final goodbye to a quite possibly dying man. Not wishing to create difficulties for Michael she decided it would be a kindness to firmly state her intention to return home that afternoon without anything more being said. Despite her decision, Michael's friends pressed her to stay for one more night, but feeling she had already imposed herself enough on their generosity, Elizabeth remained adamant that her decision should stand.

As the time approached for their departure en route to the station, Elizabeth had the first acknowledged feelings of unease and distress in the knowledge of their impending goodbye. They decided that she should catch an early evening train so they would employ their time once again slowly making their way back via the Royal Festival Hall for a last cup of tea together.

As they walked out to the road, last farewells were said with Michael's friends waving goodbye to them both from their door. Their last anxious enquiry was whether he felt able to do the journey on his own.

'I have Nurse Elizabeth to look after me!' he replied, which seemed to satisfy them but Elizabeth, not too sure that she was pleased to be so designated, realised that this impending goodbye was making her on edge and ultra-sensitive.

Companionably, arm in arm as before, they went down the road, Elizabeth once again carrying her now emptier bag. As they went, as always, they chatted, this time about his proposed visit to her home; a consistent theme of their conversation was his intention to recuperate at her house in Cornwall.

'Do you like walking?' she asked as they landed safely on the other side of the teeming traffic.

'Yes,' he replied.

'Good, we have some great walks on the cliffs and beaches nearby.'

What happy vistas opened up before her with a companionable visitor to explore the area around her home. What a great travelling companion he would make, she thought as they walked down the busy streets heading once more for the local coach station. Elizabeth was hopeful now after seeing Michael that if they were lucky there would be some months together to enjoy.

As they arrived at the corner of the main road before turning off, he stopped for a moment and said, 'Would you be able to find your way here if you came again?'

'I think so,' she said doubtfully, looking at all the streets appearing much the same. 'What type of meals do you like to eat?' she enquired as they moved off again. 'Salads, lots of salads.'

'How about prawns and baked potatoes to go with them?'

'Lovely,' he said, 'I love fish!'

Absorbed in their talk he had let go of her arm as she changed the grip from one hand to another. Realising that she was standing in the pathway of a bus which was pulling out from the kerb, Michael swiftly grabbed her to bring her to safety on the pavement.

Michael had brought with him the remainder of the bag of special chocolates she had given him, and tried to feed Elizabeth with them as they waited for their train, but she refused as she wanted him to have them all to himself, whereupon he put them away uneaten seemingly disappointed at her response.

Elizabeth was becoming increasingly saddened at their impending farewell and Michael sat silently for a great deal of the time in the train.

As the train swayed and jolted in the darkness, he would throw out an apparently disjointed word or two. On one occasion he asked her about their private place, the 'plateau' she had told him about in her letters and which he had embellished for her in one of his replies. She reassured him that she had not forgotten to put in his own piece of their plateau, and that seemed to satisfy him.

'Don't forget the foxgloves,' he added.

'No dear, I haven't forgotten them, I have put them just where you said,' and with that he seemed satisfied, once more relapsing into silence. Throughout this conversation in the semi-darkness of the tube train it crossed Elizabeth's mind that he seemed during the period of this whole visit to be giving her information about himself, his thoughts, his hopes, his dreams. At times his words were apparently unrelated to the topic on hand at the moment.

It was between one of these silent periods that Elizabeth plucked up her courage to ask him how old he was – why this mattered to her any more she could not have said and his reply confirmed that he was a few years older than herself.

As they sat side by side, they compared their hand sizes, and he told her his larger hand could spread to an octave and a half, which was useful for his piano playing. As she held up her hand for his inspection, he admired a little ring she was wearing and thought the two intertwined parts represented two dolphins.

'I thought them more like leaves,' she replied, but he reaffirmed his opinion that they looked more like dolphins, to which she replied, 'Yes Michael,' in slight mock humility.

'I love the way you say that,' came the reply causing a little glow in Elizabeth's heart.

As before, only the day before, but to Elizabeth an event which had taken place a long time ago, such was the range of emotion experienced in between then and now, they headed for the Royal Festival Hall for a last cup of tea whilst they waited for her train. In tune with Elizabeth's feelings of distress at their impending parting after such a short time together, her hand luggage seemed to have a life of its own, with the handles repeatedly twisting around causing several stops to straighten them out; for some strange reason the bag seemed heavier than the day before.

This time they joined the queue for their tray of tea together, Michael as before insisting on paying for everything despite Elizabeth's protests to share in the cost. For the first time she felt dumb and found herself searching around for topics to fill the emotional gap in their conversation which up to this moment had flowed so easily. Michael was quiet too, and seemed reluctant to move to the station. Elizabeth had to keep mentally adjusting her train departure timetable allowing more time together, but knew she would eventually have to call his attention to the fact that soon her last train would be leaving, and that he also had an appointment to keep. Elizabeth did not tell him that, due to leaving so late, she had missed her final connection at the other end, and would have to spend the night in a hotel in Exeter before proceeding on the remainder of her journey home the next day. Despite their mutual preoccupations they agreed that the time that afternoon had passed very fast, and it was Elizabeth who finally said she would definitely have to make a move right away if she was to catch the last train. Michael also realised that he was cutting things very fine indeed if he was to make the journey back across London in time for his family meeting.

'Please do not wait to say goodbye, I hate goodbyes,' she managed to say cheerfully, and he agreed with some reluctance. With her repeated assurances that she was quite alright to be left, they embraced and kissed as they had before on first meeting at the station the previous day.

'This is the painful bit,' she whispered to him as he held her close.

'Yes,' he replied as again they hugged each other. He turned and walked swiftly away leaving her by the large display board amongst the crowd of homeward bound travellers. Her eyes never left his tall figure as he walked away into the distance. At the last moment in the entrance to the Underground he turned and gave a final wave before descending out of sight to catch his train.

It was fortunate that it was now dark so no one could see the tears which slowly ran down her cheeks unchecked. On boarding her train, Elizabeth was glad that she could just close her eyes for the next few hours and relive all they had said and done together over the past two days. Although this parting was very painful, they hoped to be able to meet up somewhere halfway between them in the next few weeks, and with this happy thought she dreamed away the hours.

Chapter XIII

Minor Key

The Monday after her visit to London, Elizabeth wrote her usual letter thanking Michael for their enjoyable two days together, and then she went on to tell him of her happiness when he took her into his arms and kissed her.

That following week Elizabeth was busy with family visitors, and for some reason as the days passed, she became more and more concerned that there had been no phone call or letter from Michael to tell how he was after his strenuous days of entertaining. As each day passed with no word from Michael her concern grew, and by the end of the week her white face caused her daughter to take her aside.

'You have gone so quiet, you cannot go on like this, you'll make yourself ill. For goodness sake, phone him.'

For some reason Elizabeth felt reluctant to follow this advice as she felt that Michael's freedom in their relationship was very important and wished him to only contact her as and when he felt like it. Despite this, so she thought sensible intention, her feelings of unease increased daily until unable any longer to be in ignorance of his welfare, she finally agreed to dial his number the very next evening.

The telephone rang and rang, and after two attempts she was

finally able to get a reply. To her surprise the phone was lifted up at the other end and then placed off the hook and left there while two female voices could be heard laughing and talking. Elizabeth replaced her receiver after a minute or two thinking that at any moment someone would decide to speak to her. She tried the number again, but it soon became apparent that the telephone had not been replaced by the girls on the desk as a continual 'engaged' signal was heard. Elizabeth's feelings were now of some concern for the residents of the home; suppose an emergency arose of some sort, she fumed, and by this piece of selfishness by the staff in the reception, the nursing home telephone was unobtainable. By now her concern for Michael's welfare had reached almost fever pitch with the realisation that she was still out of touch, and now she had no means of rectifying the situation. Her feelings of helplessness amplified the already strong sensation that something was wrong.

By ten o'clock the next morning Elizabeth had become extremely worried, and having thought that breakfast would be over for the residents of the home, she dialled Michael's number. This time she was put straight through to his room.

'Who is this?' enquired an angry voice.

'Elizabeth,' she replied hurt that he did not seem to recognise her voice.

'Oh! Get off the line!' he ordered. 'I'm very busy'.

To Elizabeth, although his words were initially upsetting, she immediately realised he was very upset indeed and sought to calm him down.

'Do not speak to me like that Michael; I only rang to ask how you were'.

He straight away became calmer. 'If you really want to know how I am, everything is absolutely bloody', a phrase he would normally never have used in their conversations, and again Elizabeth realised the extent of his, as it seemed to her, panicky temper. After a minute or two of calmer conversation, and having assured him that she only needed to know he was all right, she rang off. As she replaced the receiver, Elizabeth was amazed that she was able to deal with this new aspect of their friendship. It seemed that her friend was not only having to battle with a life-threatening illness, but also with masses of forms and legal papers, which seemed to be overwhelming him. To add to these more serious problems he was also inundated with letters and cards from well-wishers, together with a continuous flow of visitors. He constantly told her that there were things he had to deal with but did not have the strength to handle them. Elizabeth was beginning to realise that whenever Michael was in trouble, she would immediately sense it.

It was from this time that Elizabeth, wishing only to help him, confined her weekly letters to short notes reassuring him of her continued understanding and support. At the same time, she repeatedly said she expected no letters or calls in response, and reiterated that she made no demands of any kind in their relationship, and from time to time only wanted assurances he was her friend.

Now was the time when Elizabeth also began to understand that her love for this increasingly dear man was not a selfish love, but was turning into a love which only wanted what was best for him, even if this meant finally having to let go. Despite these internal cogitations Elizabeth still retained the fine thread of thought implanted into her mind by the palmist who had told her that he would be with her wherever she would go. She had also been told at that time that he would definitely be with her in five to six months' time, and as the months slipped by the unlikelihood of either of these predictions becoming true seemed to increase.

At the end of the following week, a long-awaited letter addressed to Elizabeth arrived. Michael's letter was full of apologies and explanations. He was sorry he had been abrupt on the telephone, and again asked for her understanding in his present situation. His next paragraph told her of his enjoyment in their meeting and only wished it had been for longer, adding he was sorry their goodbye at Waterloo was so hasty. Concluding this short letter, he added a few more words about their visit, sending his love to her as usual.

Thankfully Elizabeth re-read this letter, and felt pleased he had regained his normal kindly nature, and more importantly to her that he had apologised for his somewhat cavalier treatment on the telephone a few days ago. She carried this letter around in her pocket for several days, sure now that their constant mind to mind communication was not broken, and was still in some way important to them both. With this knowledge she felt able to continue her weekly letters, and without prior thought or particular intention, these became more spiritual in content, answering some unspoken but strongly felt need of Michael's. The first glimmers of her role in his life were becoming more and more apparent to her as the weeks passed. It was as well that her intuition and strong faith remained unshaken in this period as it was to be over two weeks before she heard news of him again.

Chapter XIV

Recitative

It was whilst writing to Michael during this long two-week period that Elizabeth told Michael she would be staying near London visiting friends and family over the Easter period and could, if he liked, make the journey up to London whilst so comparatively near. It was to this letter that he was now replying.

The letter, when it finally arrived, was the one Elizabeth did not wish to receive. Michael wrote that he had had a setback in his health, and was not at all well at the moment. He went on to explain he was at times in considerable pain and it was a struggle to write the letter, adding as he had many times before, 'I do hope you understand.' This short note was completed by his usual, 'Love Michael.'

On receipt of this pathetic letter Elizabeth was distraught, and feeling she had to get out of the confining walls of the house, she decided to drive off to a local garden centre and walk amongst the beautiful flowers to allow herself time to calm down. The quiet walk did make her feel a little better, but still feeling the need for further quiet reflection, she stopped off at a lovely old Church on the return route home.

Fortunately, the Church door was unlocked, and on entering she found the place quiet and completely deserted. She sat down on one of the old carved bench seats to one side of the aisle and knelt in prayer, praying for her dear one. It was during these prayers that she came to realise for the first time her prayers should only be for what was best for Michael, and to leave out all her own selfish thoughts. The time to let go had now come. From this period this new found resolution accompanied her morning and evening prayers, and during many quiet moments when alone she would send up another small prayer for God to be with him in this his latest trial.

Elizabeth felt she too was in pain, and at times succumbed to the need to cry in private, a moan of pain escaping from her pent-up feelings of anguished love. At other times, when unable to retire from the presence of others, her throat ached with unshed tears. she became aware that she had been crying at some part of each day ever since he first telephoned her from his hospital bed earlier that year. At no time, despite painful thoughts and feelings, did she wish she had never met him. All these emotions she kept to herself, and was able to go about her normal life with some outward semblance of normality.

Later that same day she sat down and wrote him a letter full of love and assurances, saying that although most disappointed they could not meet at Easter, her disappointment was not for herself, but was for his being in pain and discomfort. She then referred again to their special place, their 'plateau' where the mind could escape when things were difficult, a place of beauty, colour and peace. Again, her feelings of helplessness in this situation, her inability to be of practical help, were assuaged by the notion that her contribution was of supportive and spiritual love.

In the meantime, Elizabeth was again involved with visitors from abroad, and found herself able to amuse and entertain them to their apparent satisfaction, despite her mind being absent, all thoughts far away.

It was during this week that she decided to telephone Michael, to see if she could get any news of him, not entirely sure if he would be at the nursing home or if he had been moved to the hospital as he had indicated in his last letter.

Elizabeth really did not expect to hear his voice, but hoped that the staff at the nursing home would give her the address of the hospital to where he had been moved. She knew before she dialled the number that the staff would not normally divulge this type of information to anyone other than the closest of relatives and friends, and could see she might have a problem in finding out exactly where he had been sent.

Almost as soon as the telephone rang, his voice, quieter and rather subdued could be heard, and after asking him how he was, he told her he had seen the doctors at the hospital who had given him the impression that there was no more hope. His voice sounded rather grim as he told her exactly what had been said. The doctors had not told him in so many words, but this was the definite impression he had been given. Elizabeth could tell that all hope had gone out of his voice and seeking to cheer him a little asked him how he was feeling about visitors, wondering whether he would like to see her again.

'No, I don't want to see anybody, only my closest friends!'

His honesty on this occasion hit Elizabeth like a blow, and Michael realising she was made very unhappy by this frank remark, amended this statement by saying he would rather spend time with her than almost anyone he knew. He went on to say whilst she quietly listened, still in pain at this last remark, 'No more phone calls to see how I am.'

There was a silence whilst Elizabeth called together all her emotional strength and then asked quietly, 'Do you want me to keep on writing?'

Michael appeared to think about this, and after a few moments thought said, 'Yes, you can keep writing.' Admittedly, Elizabeth had bridled slightly at his remark about phone calls as she could only remember ringing him two or three times in the months she had known him, but allowed it to pass. The distress of them both at the finality of his words left Elizabeth speechless in her pain and grief, and she realised their conversation was becoming very fraught on both sides.

'I can only ever offer you spiritual love,' he added as she made her heartfelt farewell.

'God bless you dear.'

The telephone went quiet for a moment, and then in a very low voice he said, 'I always wanted to come you know,' and her reply, 'Yes dear, I know,' left the air between them quiet, both reluctant to say that last goodbye. Finally, not wishing to further traumatise them both, Elizabeth replaced the receiver slowly and quietly, overwhelmed by the way their conversation had gone; feelings of almost total rejection uppermost in her mind.

Shocked beyond measure, Elizabeth fell into a storm of weeping and finally had to call on her friend Diana to help her come to terms with her intense grief. She felt in these hours as if she had passed through some dreadful nightmare only to be told that they had never met and that everything was as it always had been, the events of the past eight months a mirage of reality. Diana put her to bed with a sedative and waited until she was sure she had finally fallen asleep, and then quietly left the house.

The next day, calmer thoughts filtered in as Elizabeth,

acknowledging to herself that as Michael was, as he said in severe pain, and in all probability under heavy medication, his usually calm and friendly nature was not surprisingly upset. She could not possibly imagine his thoughts and emotions at this time. She surmised that it was only natural he would act in this way, and was able to comfort herself that her role as friend did not preclude her from praying with all her strength for alleviation of his suffering in whatever way God thought was best for him. Several times that day she fell into prayer, beseeching God to help him in this time of his great need.

When the next day came for her usual weekly letter, a letter which she had given much thought, she felt the need to express the feelings that their last, very last phone call had left with her. Now there seemed very little time left, she felt that she could not leave unspoken, or ignore, her strongly felt emotions, and so she sat down to write:

'My dear Michael, after our telephone conversation the other night lots of different thoughts have been floating through my head… do not worry when you say you are not the man you were, I think you need to read your Shakespeare: "Love is not love which alters when it alteration finds, or bends with the remover to remove: O, no! It is an ever-fixed mark, that looks on tempests and is never shaken." I think we had discussed enough on this subject to agree it has very many facets, and as far as I am concerned it is a state of being, unqualified, uncomplicated, un-dissected, and better so and just accepted as a blessing freely given with no expectations, no stinting in quality or quantity. For me it flows like a stream of life, uncritical and unchanging. If this is 'spiritual love', then so be it.

Her letter concluded, 'Please, dear Michael, accept me as I am, and if I can count as one of your friends, I am more than satisfied,' signing herself in her usual way, 'Love Elizabeth.'

When Elizabeth sealed this letter and posted it off, she knew there would be neither a reply nor a telephone call to let her know how he received her thoughts on the subject of love.

When two weeks had again passed with no news of any kind, Elizabeth decided it would be quite natural to telephone Michael's friends with whom she had spent the night whilst visiting him in London, hoping they would have some up- to- date news of his progress. She was immediately glad that she had called as they had just that moment come from visiting him, and were able to comfort Elizabeth with the news that he had told nearly all his friends to stay away, which made her feel a little better. However, their news, telling her he was very deeply depressed, saddened her greatly, an added burden for him to bear.

After this conversation with Michael's old friends Elizabeth felt more able to write her usual Monday letters, and for some reason she never could explain later, she decided to respond to a letter written earlier in the year, when he had told her of how he had decided to believe in God, illustrating this by a little diagram of a see-saw just tilted down in the direction of his word 'God' opposed to the side which he had labelled 'Nothing'. She had noticed that his little cross was placed only just to the right of the fulcrum, and wished and hoped that she could cause him to mentally place his 'X' right down to the outer end to show his affirmation of his complete faith in God.

She opened her letter in her normal affectionate way, and after a few semi-trivial remarks about a local event, went on to say, 'Of course all this time I am wondering how you are, and wondering too if my letters hold any interest for you, or even perhaps some words of comfort.' As she wrote, the words were forming in her head and they started to flow as she launched into sharing with Michael her most private self. She realised as she wrote that in their very earliest long telephone conversation she had very briefly touched on this particular subject, but until now it had never been mentioned again. She continued, 'I remember in one of your letters from hospital that you told me how you had 'decided on God' and illustrated this with a see-saw with the 'X' just tilting the balance to one side. With this in mind, and knowing that you felt able to confide these thoughts to me, I will now tell you of a (to me) remarkable event which did not change my belief in another life, but enhanced it by so closely touching my state of mind at that time.'

'The day the event took place was much as any other except I was to go to an outlying village to view a cottage much in need of repair and meet my father who was to give me his advice as to whether it was a viable purchase. At this time, I was probably still grappling with the daunting fact that I was going to have to bring up four children alone. My father, as always, was late for our appointment so I decided to re-visit the Church which was very close by while I waited. The day was chilly and I was glad to be getting out of the very cold wind. I quickly walked down the avenue of yews and approached the heavy Church door, and finding it unlocked, stepped inside. The Church was empty and very cool on this March morning. Interested in the history of the Church and local families whose monuments were usually placed around the ancient walls, I looked about me and started to walk around commencing with the back of the Church to the left of the door. My attention was soon drawn to a life-size fresco or painting

(I cannot remember which) of an Elizabethan lady, and I studied the details closely. She wore a chatelaine at her waist and her dress was beautifully embroidered with the flowers of the field which I love so much. Below her, as is the custom in plaques or brasses, could be seen the smaller figures of children in descending size. The first thing which caught my attention, apart from the beauty of her dress, was the fact that no figure of an Elizabethan man accompanied the obviously maternal figure of the lady. I looked closer to read the words cut into the brass plaque below and although I cannot remember now the exact details, they conveyed to me that she was a local landowner and much respected in the neighbourhood for her charitable works. The fact that she had apparently achieved all this alone held deep significance for me and from that time I made a resolve that I could achieve all I wanted, even if I had to do it all by myself. I seemed to gaze for some time at the beautiful lady before resuming my perambulation round the remainder of the Church where I found nothing further of great interest. I then stepped outside and found my father waiting for me, and we departed to look at the cottage'.

Elizabeth saw she had not mentioned the fact that the lady's dress was in lovely colours, the embroidery exquisitely done, but decided that with her need to keep her letters to Michael as short as possible, continued with her story -

'Quite some time after this visit to the Church, I went to visit old family friends, the husband a local historian, a very interesting person to talk to. Whilst there he asked me if I had seen the new book on the subject of old brasses and other commemorative plaques in West Country Churches. We leafed through the book together, and later left alone, I again eagerly dipped into the pages once more. When I had finished, I said, '"But why has the author not included the wonderful one in the local Church? I have never seen anything so beautiful,"" and went on to describe it in detail. My old friend looked rather surprised, but being far too polite to contradict me, kindly went through the book with me once more. Again, he asked me to describe what I had seen, together with details of the position of this memorial. Finally, he had to tell me that there was no such lady in the Church, which was in the main quite unremarkable in this respect. Truly astonished, and feeling there had to be a mistake, sometime later, I took the opportunity to re-visit the Church and discovered to my shock only a large blank wall! I searched the Church to make sure I had made no mistake in the location and to my disappointment found absolutely nothing. By now of course, I had come to realise that I had received a vision which told me in terms that I could receive how I was to proceed in the future. This vision of the Lady, as I called her, has never left me. I can still see her wonderful dress so richly embroidered although seen so long ago."

Then, starting a new paragraph she thoughtfully went on to write:

'The reason dear Michael for telling you my story, is to share one of the most significant events of my life, which has had a deep and profound effect on the twenty-five years which followed. I still remain astonished that such a remarkable favour was received by such an ordinary person as myself. It must have been during those intervening years from then till now that I took hold of the golden thread which leads me across the plateau."

Feeling that she had given him her heart she sent her love and signed it as usual, 'Elizabeth.' Before she could change her mind as to its contents, she sealed the letter down, hoping with all her heart that it would in some way help him.

That week she had occasion to go to the funeral of a very old friend and decided to go and buy a navy blue hat to match her summer suit. The light straw hat of her choice was found with ease, the shape almost identical to the old red hat previously admired by Michael; he would like this, she thought, as she twirled it around on her finger to view it from every angle.

All that weekend Elizabeth felt very uneasy, physical symptoms of occasional stomach cramps increased her sensations of unease.

'I feel as if I am expecting to hear from Michael any moment,' she told Diana over a morning coffee together.

It was true; she had been hoping to see one of his envelopes shoot through the door with the rest of her morning mail in the past few days. The reasons for this notion she could not imagine, he certainly had given her no reason whatever to think she would be hearing from him again.

On Saturday night Elizabeth had fallen into profound prayer, repeating her prayers for Michael's release from suffering and the very deep depression he was experiencing. At the end of these supplications she had the strangest compulsion to lift her arms above her head as if to draw Heaven's power to her aid like the prophets of old. I have never done that before, she realised, surprised at her actions as she finally went to bed.

Monday was the day for her weekly letter, and as she sat down at her desk the feeling of being out of communication still persisted, but despite this she managed to put together a cheerful descriptive letter telling Michael about a recent walk along the beach. The letter finished, she posted it off, hoping he would not notice the lack of natural flow in her words. She felt very dissatisfied with her letter, and wondered if the weeks of silence were having an effect on her writing, a thing that had never bothered her before.

The telephone rang at mid-day on Tuesday. It was Michael's friends, the friends she had stayed with, to tell her that he had died peacefully on the Monday morning, at just about the time she had sat down to write her letter, that letter she had found so difficult to write. It seemed to her that her strong intuition where he was concerned had not let her down, and she had already known instinctively that he would not be reading this, her final letter.

To Elizabeth's surprise she felt nothing but happiness in that first week of bereavement, only glad at last that Michael was out of pain, no longer suffering from mental anguish as he came to realise that his normally fit body had finally let him down, and as he had described it himself, allowing this disgusting thing to grow inside him. Nevertheless, he suddenly seemed very far away from her, their fine line of communication finally cut.

With the encouragement of Michael's friends in London, Elizabeth decided to once again make the long journey for his funeral and pay her last respects. All was arranged that she would once again stay with them for the night, and so she packed her navy blue suit and that hat, bought only last week for her old friend's funeral, now to be worn at Michael's. She wanted to look at her smart best for him, as she described it to herself.

The journey up to London awakened so many happy memories of the recent past, the changeover of trains at Salisbury reviving painfully intense emotions hard to conceal from her fellow passengers. She gained control of the tears by steadfastly looking out of the window, so her face was averted for the duration of the second half of the journey.

The welcome at the end of her journey left her in no doubt of the affection these kind people bore Michael, and by association, Elizabeth herself. Despite all their attention Elizabeth had great difficulty in sleeping, in fact during the night feeling so ill she almost had to call for help, thinking that she would need a doctor. By a great effort of will, and doing as she had told Michael in days past, she took her mind to their special place, their plateau, and so, finally, was able to sleep for a few hours. Despite this poor start to her night she awoke perfectly calm, and well able to face the day ahead; she could not let Michael down now.

Next morning, they were driven to a small chapel situated in a cemetery, the simplest of venues; how like him to have chosen such a place for his own funeral, she thought, sure in her heart that this was his own choice.

Elizabeth sat with her friends close to where the coffin lay covered with beautiful cream and white roses. The words and music of the simple service caused such a surge of emotion that it was with great difficulty that she was able to preserve her outward composure by fixing her gaze on the trees moving about in the gentle breeze just glimpsed through an opposite window. Nevertheless, her nearest neighbour, sensing her distress, quietly asked if she was alright. She briefly nodded, not daring to utter a word. Whilst the address was being given Elizabeth contemplated the coffin, trying to imagine him lying there, but was unable to do so, so sure that 'he' was not there. All that was left were the outer remains of his earthly body, no longer inhabited.

The beautifully spoken words of the twenty-third Psalm held extra poignancy for her, the words, 'He makes me lie down in green pastures. He leads me beside still waters; he restores my soul,' recalled their shared 'plateau' acting as balm to her soul at this moment of great personal sorrow.

Because Elizabeth wished to talk to as many of Michael's friends and family as possible, but nevertheless wishing to remain at the same time in the background and not intrude on the family's own grief, she consented to attend the reception held in a nearby hotel. During conversation with his family she asked if her letters could be returned to her at some time, and they promised to forward these to her in due course.

It was quite evident to Elizabeth, shown by the presence of so many of Michael's friends and family, that he was highly esteemed, and she could only concur in her heart, knowing the value she herself put on his character and abilities. As is so often the case, Elizabeth found this meeting of family and friends comforting and almost enjoyable with all the reminiscences and tales told of her friend, showing her many new aspects of the man she loved.

As the funeral took place in the morning, Elizabeth was able to leave directly after the refreshments at the hotel, departing earlier than most of the other guests. She felt that it was best for her, such a new friend, to leave his older friends and family to remember him on their own.

Chapter XV

Pianissimo

The journey home was uneventful. Elizabeth seemed to be in a dreamy reflective state, her mind pleasantly in a state of limbo. and so she dreamt the day away until she left the train at Exeter Station.

With several hours to spare before catching her next connection, she decided to walk up to the city from the station; it was a pleasant day and her overnight bag was fairly light. She traversed the busy main road and climbed up the steep pavements leading past the University campus into the city proper.

The inner city was busy and the pavements full of Friday shoppers when Elizabeth suddenly heard a loud bang behind her. Sure that something very like a large cardboard carton had either been dropped or thrown from above one of the nearby high buildings she swiftly turned around, and to her surprise saw not only that the street behind her was completely empty for several yards, but there was no sign whatever of any object lying on the pavement to explain the loud noise. She turned back to proceed on her way aiming for a nearby café when she distinctly felt the sensation of a finger running down the whole length of her spine, touching, so it seemed, her jacket but not firm enough to actually touch the skin. She again turned around to assure herself that no one was anywhere near her and went on her way mystified, but for some reason feeling that this seemed to have a connection with Michael. She had never previously received any such direct kind of supernatural communication except the vision she had told Michael about in her last, hopefully received letter.

Elizabeth's euphoric dream-like state remained with her for the rest of that day, and as the days passed, this 'out of this world' feeling persisted whenever she was alone. In quiet moments when with others, her gaze would drift to a window, her thoughts immediately suspended, and she would once more slip into this state. She continued for many weeks dwelling in another realm of happy, pleasant and extremely peaceful thoughts.

At this time the only regret in Elizabeth's life was the possibility that Michael had either not received, or been well enough to read her last letter, telling him of her vision in the Church, and how it had changed her life forever. For some reason these words had assumed a great importance to her as she had felt at the time that they would be of enormous comfort to him and reinforce his belief in the afterlife.

When the packet containing her letters arrived, returned to her as promised, she found amongst them the important last letter with the envelope slit open, and this gave her some comfort that it had indeed been received and possibly even read before he died. All her energies at that time had been to divert his thoughts away from his profound depression of the last weeks. She had also felt that if she could only give him a few minutes or even seconds of relief it would have been something.

In between carrying out her normal life, as she was able to recognise in an automatic way, Elizabeth was receiving definite sensations that Michael was calling her attention to the fact he was around. Eventually, Elizabeth became rather concerned that she was imagining these small events, most of them easily explained away in a rational light, and she felt she was being drawn into some realm of knowledge quite new to her. At this time, she also came to realise that throughout the months since their meeting her emotional range had expanded far beyond any heights or depths previously experienced, and in the final weeks of his life she had discovered parts of her soul unguessed at. She felt a veil had been torn from her eyes. It was because of this new enlightenment that she was now no longer able to allow her usually rather conventional and slightly sceptical soul to rule out the possibility that she was indeed still in communication with the man she loved, even if this communication was now in a different medium, like a different type of language. Her certainties became stronger as she remembered the words of the burial service – 'I am the resurrection and the life, saith the Lord; he that believeth in me, though he were dead, yet shall he live; and whosoever liveth and believeth in me shall never die.' She remembered too other words from the burial service, words which now for the first time leapt into life becoming suddenly full of meaning for her – 'There are also celestial bodies, and bodies terrestrial,' followed by the Collect which promises, 'In whom whosoever believeth shall live, though he die; and whosoever liveth, and believeth in him, shall not die eternally.' The comfort derived from these words was enormous and served to yet again open Elizabeth's eyes to the fact that all the time the Christian Church believed what she had so recently and so painfully come to realise, that sorrow for those who have gone before us is only for ourselves who are left behind.

At no time was Elizabeth worried or frightened by any of these sensations she had been experiencing of Michael's presence, but viewed them rather as a fascinated spectator wondering where all this was leading to, if anywhere.

It was in this period soon after the funeral that Elizabeth received the first of two dreams. The clarity of these dreams remained sharply bright the next day, and in fact the second dream was so clear and important to her that it actually woke her up, her subconscious clamouring for her to awaken and remember each part in exact detail. She looked at the clock beside her bed and saw that she had in fact only been asleep for less than two hours.

The first of these dreams was of her friend Michael; she saw him lying on a bed in which he half reclined, and he apologised for not rising but said he was not quite recovered yet, and asked her to introduce him to all her family. This dream left her with a happiness that he had made such contact with her and that all was well with him.

The second dream took place two weeks later and was longer and very important in her eyes. It seemed she was lying down out in the open, perhaps on a sun bed. One of her daughters was nearby, and a very close friend was picking bunches of primroses one or two fields away. It seemed Michael's voice, although not immediately recognised by her at first, said to her, 'Give me your left leg and turn yourself around to face the other way,' and without much ado he took hold of her left leg and turned her around. Then he said, 'Go forward and look into that pool of water before you.' She did as he asked, and, looking into the quiet pool, first saw her own face mirrored there, and to one side that of her youngest daughter. Whilst she watched, Michael's unmistakable face rose like the sun or moon between them. The shock of this dream drew her instantly from her sleep, and as she awoke a voice in her head said, 'Don't forget your hat!' which confirmed beyond anything that this was more than just a fantasy. Next day the recollection of this dream, so vivid in her mind, made her laugh to herself at

Michael's typical lack of ceremony in taking her leg and spinning her around.

The combination of these two dreams confirmed her feeling that they were special to each other as quite evidently he was attempting to make contact with her. During her life Elizabeth had at times experienced a dream of a close friend or relative who had recently died, dreams always remembered. These quite rare dreams seemed to be a message of comfort that all was well with them, but never before had she received such a personal type of dream with its evident message, 'Here I am, alive and well,' with the additional information, now so important to her: 'We are still in communication.' Normally Elizabeth's dreams, as she surmised was usually the case with most people, would immediately disappear upon awakening, and even with an effort these could not be recalled, however pleasant they may have been. These recollected dreams in relation to Michael, or as she termed them messages, were remembered in exact detail, and then could be recalled months or even many years later with no effort at all of any kind. It was becoming evident to her that Michael wished her to be aware of him in every way possible.

Over the next few days the realisation slowly dawned on Elizabeth that love does not die; in fact it was possible for it to live and grow. This understanding was of enormous comfort to her at this time; she now knew without a doubt that the actual physical presence of the loved one was not essential for this growth.

* * *

With her family's encouragement Elizabeth decided to make a short trip abroad to visit friends living in Germany, and as the airport was not far from her father's house, resolved that a short visit with him before her departure would be opportune.

The by now very well-known journey with all its changes of coach and rail, went by as usual, with Elizabeth unable to view her arrival at Salisbury station with anything else but pain.

Extremely tired upon arrival, Elizabeth saw with satisfaction that her father was being very well cared for and was very pleased to see her, only sorry that her visit was to be so short. She promised to return after her few days away in Germany, and with this the old man seemed almost content.

Elizabeth's father retired early each night, and with the carers withdrawing to their own private part of the house she sat down in a wing-backed chair and slipped off her shoes to ease her aching feet. Pulling her stockinged feet up in much the same posture as she had in Michael's room when she visited him in London, and peaceful but tired, she leant her head back and closed her eyes. Almost at once a feeling of intense spiritual communication seemed to take place with Michael's spirit. It felt as if her entire being was drawn out of her body and swiftly rose to meet his spirit. A sensation of most pure and exquisite ecstasy washed over her whole being and held her motionless in her chair, transfixed by this sweet gift to her soul as she was bathed and enfolded in his love. The beauty of these moments would never be forgotten. Prompted eventually by some sensation telling her that she had to break off this soul to soul meeting, and comforted, she quietly departed for bed, astonished by this new gift showing her that Michael was with her still. By now her inner certainty that he was still very much part of her life, although not seen, was becoming stronger each day. This last precious gift she realised would probably never be repeated and for this reason knew she would treasure the remembrance for the rest of her life.

The next day on her flight over the Channel and her long wait at Cologne /Bonn Airport she reflected on this further expansion of her spiritual horizons, and having upon occasion a slightly ribald turn of mind, explained to herself the sensations she had experienced the night before as being like the climax of a particularly loving sexual experience, but much more spiritually beautiful.

It seemed to her that the connection she had dimly perceived on first meeting Michael, expanded and explored by them both during his life in her letters and their conversations, was for a definite purpose. Elizabeth began to feel that this purpose could have enormous significance and importance for her future in determining the direction her path in life would take her.

As the days passed on her return home this certainty increased, but up to that moment her future was veiled and unseen. Nevertheless, this future without a doubt must in some way encompass Michael's life and work.

By now, Elizabeth feeling so sure that Michael was near, started to converse with him in her mind, at first feeling rather foolish, but with all the recent events showing his presence to her, she began to gain confidence that their minds were indeed still in contact.

These events of great spirituality did not lessen Elizabeth's tears although their duration was shorter, some days better than others. When she was tired or dispirited the tears would flow, and her loss seemed new again. Elizabeth surprised herself that she did not rail at heaven for taking the man she truly loved away from her just as they had found each other. At other times the remembrance of his physical and mental sufferings seemed unbearable and would bring on a storm of weeping which left her exhausted and forlorn. On the other hand she felt she had completed her task, her role in his life, and thought that if that did not make her feel happy now, she knew in time it would do so. The conviction that their life together was to continue in another dimension would not go away.

At this time, her desire to talk to anyone who would listen about her loved one was discouraged by nearly all her family who would, after an embarrassed silence, change the subject, leaving her wishing she had not brought the matter up. To have been permitted to introduce his name naturally into a conversation would have helped her enormously, but circumstances prevented even his existence in her life to be common knowledge, and therefore such a situation very rarely arose. She had noticed a similar difficulty amongst her recently bereaved friends, who were left isolated by those around them due to their embarrassment, and perhaps a feeling of delicacy, preventing any mention of the loved one's name.

Her only safety valve was the continued support of her friend Diana who listened uncritically to all she had to say with little comment. However, Elizabeth's most intimate spiritual experiences she kept to herself, feeling even Diana would find them unbelievable. Elizabeth also felt that any sharing of these special moments would somehow be a betrayal of Michael and would in some way sully their relationship, making it ordinary, even possibly a cause for derision and laughter in others.

During this period Elizabeth found she had to make a great many mental adjustments. She had been brought up in the Church of England, and had always understood that what she was entering into was not exactly within the scope of their teaching. She had already in the early days of her meeting Michael visited the palmist in her anxiety as to where the friendship was going, and had understood that the Church frowned on such dabbling in the occult as she would have termed it then. Also, up to that time she had always stoutly maintained that it was far better not to know what fate had in store for her or anyone else. Certainly some of the future events in her young life had been far better concealed from her; otherwise she would not have been able to contemplate them in advance, so difficult and at times extremely distressing had these events been, her heart would have failed her. Now, here, led by her love for this man, a love which had expanded her awareness and shown her horizons unknown, she had been taken by the hand by his spirit to reveal that we are all immortal, and when we die we are still there, but unseen. Elizabeth could well remember long ago an old doctor friend of the family explaining to the young girl, as she was then, that the dead had merely gone into another room where they were unseen by those left behind, but still close by. Elizabeth herself had explained to her grieving questing children, when the loss of a dearly loved Granny brought them for the first time face to face with death, that it was just like an old coat being cast away, no longer needed, and they did not need to worry as Granny was not there in the coffin, but in a better place. This was Elizabeth's thinking before she had lost her best friend, but now she had to make a great step forward, a leap of faith – Michael was there with her, or was she imagining it? Was the death of her loved one leading her to imaginary thoughts, wishful thinking on her part? Her heart and mind clung almost in desperation to the growing belief that he was indeed by her side. Was this the meaning of the palmist's words which had puzzled her so much at the time, that he would never leave her, that he would be with her wherever she went? She realised with some shock that the prediction that he would be with her in not less than six months

– and further recalled that the palmist had corrected herself and said a little earlier than that, probably five months – that this exactly fitted in with the time that Michael had died.

Elizabeth's need to consult someone soon became daily more apparent, her cogitations becoming more confused as time passed. The niggling idea at the back of her mind was that all her feelings for Michael had misled her into imagining that he returned her love; their last fraught telephone conversation when he told her he did not want to see her again laying like a wound on her sensibilities. His offering her only, as he put it, 'spiritual love' seemed at the time a poor recompense for human love.

Grief, she was discovering, was not like a bad case of measles which would go away in time; it had many forms and stages. The need to understand what was happening to her in this her first experience in her long life of profound grief led her to search the library shelves for guidance and understanding, finding that books on aspects of spirituality were hard to find. Her need was a hunger that could not be satisfied. The few books she was able to find she devoured at speed as she came to realise she was not alone in finding this aspect of the human experience one of the most difficult to be lived with. In years past when this subject of grief and grieving had come up in normal conversation she had glibly stated that 'one learns to live with it' without the slightest idea how very difficult this 'living with it' could become.

Chapter XVI
Coda

On Elizabeth's return from her brief break away in Germany, she planned to go on a round of visits to old friends, some of whom she had not seen for many years, but with whom she had corresponded on an annual basis. She knew that in the past year particularly she had neglected her friends to a shameful degree, and now thought it was time to try and rebuild her life. It was only by being ceaselessly occupied that she felt able to continue with her daily life, and travel and new places helped to fill that ever present void in her world.

Still in the dreamlike state that had persisted since Michael's death, she let herself undertake her round of visits, enjoying her reunions with old friends, but somehow not really a part of what was going on around her. She felt she was viewing events at a distance and was not really involved in them. The effort to appear alive and interested cost her a great deal. She hoped that they did not notice the lack of her usual outgoing personality, nor could guess that she had suffered such a recent personal loss and was trying very hard to come to terms with her grief.

It was whilst on this round of visits that she finally went to stay with the godmother of her youngest daughter. Here she met up with her daughter who was already staying there on a visit. Elizabeth had known this friend for, probably over forty years, they both agreed, after recalling earliest meetings when they were both young women, Elizabeth at that time with small children, and her friend then engaged to marry her future husband. Now this friend was a widow of some years, and was able to help and sympathise with Elizabeth's feelings of bereavement. Apart from this already close connection of many years, Elizabeth remembered with great clarity that she had appeared picking primroses, together with her own daughter, in the second of her vivid dreams of Michael. There had to be some type of connection she felt sure, but could not at the time unravel the link.

Because Helen had great abilities of understanding, Elizabeth felt able to confide all that had passed in that year, and the final days of her loss. She knew her friend was a very spiritual person, her loving and gay personality reached bounds which Elizabeth could not, she had to admit to herself, attain. She never let anyone in need with whom she came into contact go away empty-handed; she gave of herself, her time and all she possessed in the helping of others.

One evening of this visit the two of them sat on the large sofa together and being alone for the whole evening, Elizabeth finally felt able to tell her friend how troubled she felt by the dreams and other happenings that had occurred since Michael's death. Finally, Helen broached a subject she knew Elizabeth had shied away from over the years, the subject of clairvoyants and mediums.

Elizabeth knew that Helen was in the habit of involving herself in the world of spirit guides, but also knew that her main reason for this type of connection was to participate in the spiritual healing of others.

'I am becoming absolutely sure that all this has been meant, and if I felt that it was for nothing I would be devastated,' Elizabeth told Helen.

She resumed after a thoughtful pause, her friend sitting quietly making no comment, as she knew that Elizabeth had to take time to put into words her obviously deeply held feelings.

'I feel,' Elizabeth resumed, 'I feel God has a purpose, something he wants me to do, perhaps something to do with Michael, maybe to help others – I really do not know exactly how or what,' she finished helplessly.

Helen, seeing her emotional need, turned and held her hand comfortingly, and they sat quietly for a few minutes saying nothing. Sensing her friend's continuing distress and bewilderment, Helen turned to look Elizabeth straight in the face and said earnestly, 'I think you ought to see my friend Angela, a medium; she is a wonderful person particularly involved in spiritual healing.'

Elizabeth's natural deeply felt caution was now completely disregarded in her present need. She eagerly enquired. 'Do you think she would see me?' Helen nodded and said, 'Why don't you try and see her whilst you are here? She lives only twenty-five miles away, and I could drive you there.'

Seeing an immediate spark of interest mixed with hope in Elizabeth's face, she added, 'I should warn you, she is very much in demand, and maybe she will not be able to see you this time, so you must come and stay with me again, and I will take you to see her when the time is right.. It would be good for me to visit too' she added seeing Elizabeth was about to protest at these arrangements which would involve her ever generous friend in time and expense. 'I need to see her myself for some more healing on a hip problem I have,' and without letting Elizabeth open her mouth again, she hurried off to telephone right away.

After a few moments she came back smiling. 'She can see you tomorrow at four o'clock as she has had a cancellation,' and went on quickly noting the expressive face of her friend where conflicting thoughts appeared in rapid succession. 'Now you must not be concerned, you will not find her dressed in weird garments gazing into a crystal ball; you will like her I am sure, she is much in demand for her work in healing.'

Elizabeth's daughter decided to come with them for the ride, and so the trio, always happy in each other's company, set off after an early lunch. The roads were busy as it was the school holidays and many caravans and cars loaded with families were obviously setting off for the coast. Nevertheless, despite the busy road, the drive was pleasant, with Helen skilfully driving through the continuous stream of traffic, which required all her concentration.

Elizabeth's thoughts drifted to the impending interview. There were so many unanswered questions left over from her brief relationship with Michael, she hoped she might soon be given some insight into the answers to those questions. As instructed, she had that morning purchased a new cassette as she understood her hour long interview would be taped for her so she could listen to it afterwards at her leisure. She appreciated this idea as this would have been useful when she saw the palmist the year before, it was so easy to forget what was said or misinterpret half-forgotten information, she mused as they sped along the now leafy, tree-lined roads leading to the medium's home. She imagined that her forthcoming interview would be conducted in much the same manner as at that earlier palm reading the year before.

It had been agreed that Helen would take her goddaughter off for a cup of tea and look around the shops whilst Elizabeth had her meeting with Angela.

By now Elizabeth was beginning to feel as if she had an appointment with the dentist, and rather dreaded the moment when the other two would leave her alone with a strange woman, in a strange house, in a strange town.

Nearly all this stage fright left her when they drove up to the modest end of terrace house and were greeted by a charming young woman who, after affectionately embracing Helen, and introductions having been made to the other two, shook their hands in a cordial and friendly way. They were all conducted into her garden, which was full of roses and bright flowers spilling out of tubs. Elizabeth, looking around her, felt immediately in accord with the owner of this attractive environment full of colour, light and fragrant scents. She could not resist bending down to smell the roses as she passed down the garden path, lingering behind the others as they all wended their way to where some tables and chairs were set out in the sunshine. After some conversation, and much laughter, Helen told Angela of her plan to go into town with her godchild whilst the interview took place and agreed that she would only be away for an hour or so. As they left, Elizabeth followed the young medium into the house, once again feeing all the sensations of a dental appointment, still not sure in her mind that she was doing the right thing in seeking this interview. At least I shan't have to worry about the drill, she joked with herself as they entered the house.

Angela led her into what seemed to be the front room, filled with comfortable easy chairs and sofas. As Elizabeth looked around she saw all the signs that this room was used as the family sitting room. A large vase of flowers, arranged in an informal and pleasant manner, was situated in a bay window, evidently picked from the abundant garden seen through the window outside. The very normality of the bright and light room allowed some of the tension to leave Elizabeth's body as Angela gestured her to the sofa and said, 'Please sit anywhere you feel comfortable,' and went over to close the door shut behind them. 'Have you got the tape?' she asked as she seated herself in an easy chair opposite Elizabeth at a comfortable distance as in a social setting. Elizabeth got up and handed this over, and Angela placed it into a small hand-held recorder.

'Before we start, I think I should explain one or two things,' she said. 'How do you feel about all this?' she asked looking enquiringly at Elizabeth.

'I have to admit,' she responded slowly in her low expressive voice, not wishing to offend the enquirer, 'I have not been very happy about this sort of thing in the past. I once knew a lady who was using someone as a medium, and this person was very unhappy about the situation, and did not like the work which was frightening her.' Seeing Angela's sober attention she added, 'I felt, and do still feel that this situation should never have arisen and was very wrong, especially as the person involved was slightly mentally disabled.'

'I quite agree,' Angela responded, 'There are some charlatans around and they do a great deal of harm.'

With this point settled she went on to explain that she worked with a group of people on the other side that would come into whatever conversation which took place. At times some of these spirits only spoke in a foreign language, and this would involve at times a long pause in the conversation while their words were translated for her. Seeing now that she had Elizabeth's full attention, Angela went on to explain that she could hear their voices on a power line much like a telephone line. Finally she added, 'Please do not tell me anything about yourself, it only confuses things,' and Elizabeth nodded, pleased that this point had been made.

Her enquiry, 'Has Helen told you anything about me?' elicited the quick reply that nothing had been passed on to her except the desire to see her. Now feeling more confident that here was a person she could trust, she awaited with great interest, and some hope, the things that would be revealed to her.

Angela tested the tape by the accustomed method of 'testing, testing, one, two, three,' in a clear voice, and upon re-winding the tape and hearing her own words repeated, opened the proceedings by saying, 'I really feel I should make the introductions first before we start,' and went on to say, 'May we say to you that it is a joy that you have joined us and we are very glad you have come to have a conversation with us.' Elizabeth, not entirely sure what type of conversation was to ensue, sat attentively to listen to Angela's next words: 'We have not drawn together today to tell you anything, we have drawn together to have a conversation in order to give you confidence to step off your springboard.'

She then paused and appeared to be listening in the most natural way possible; it was evident that she was listening to more than one person, and turning her body slightly, seemed to be speaking to someone else.

'We have met before? Yes, we have met before, that is why you came to see me last week,' and then explained to Elizabeth, 'We have a gentleman here, who not long ago moved over and, is extremely well and happy, who we hope you are becoming consciously aware is following you around, because he is working very hard for you and on behalf of you, and the first and foremost thing he wants you to know is that he is extremely well.'

These words made Elizabeth sit up, never having expected that she would make any sort of direct contact with Michael, sure at this moment that it was him who was speaking to her. As always, she mentally told herself that she should be cautious, and only if information came through of such a private nature only known to them both, would she indeed be sure that she was not the victim of a practised deceiver. Her instincts told her that Angela was everything that she appeared to be, an attractive, natural, but most fortunate young woman who had been given a great gift of seeing and hearing more than most humans are privileged to know.

Angela continued with her conversation in her expressive voice adding, 'And he is sorry, as far as sorry, whatever that word means, for the pain you have felt, but obviously there are things that are designated and designed for us that we cannot fight, and obviously this was one of them.'

She paused here, and then brightening her tone continued: 'Now we have a lot of people joining us, yes I know, I explained to Elizabeth I called you the 'God Squad', yes. I did, I have already done that. I am being told that you have many craft talents, a very talented woman, but you need to move beyond that now, there are other places to go. I also see publications; I see that you have written books but there are other types of books you need to write; certainly books to help women, you have a very great gift to help women, and you would also be able to write the most exquisite book that, whilst it may be sold as fiction, is true to life, that many women could hold on to and think, I can relate to that, I will take that with me, yes, and this book must be written, we would say from our words, for us it is your choice whether you write it, but we feel it really should be written. Here Elizabeth felt the need to clarify what had been said, feeling not for the first time some embarrassment at the turn the conversation was taking - 'Am I allowed to say something?' 'Of course, have the conversation...' 'Well, it relates to this person who has been following me around, I do not know if he approves or not that our story should be told.'

'Absolutely.'

'Really? It involves him...'

'Absolutely, chance meetings, finding the person, opens up

a section of our soul that we did not know was there.' Angela resumed after a pause, 'It doesn't just open up a new chapter, it opens up a new life, and we must never see life in terms of how many years we have been alive earthbound, because life is eternal and you know you will meet again.' 'Will we?' asked Elizabeth. 'Yes, because he will wait now, however long it takes.' 'Will he?' 'Yes, that is why he is here, he is putting his hand out saying, "You are my angel and I will wait forever for my angel."

'I am no angel,' interposed Elizabeth, feeling once again somewhat embarrassed at being named thus.

'Ah, you are his angel.'

'I am a very human person.'

'But you need to understand the feeling of someone meeting their angel, because it is – we use the words very badly because you put yourself down and that it is very naughty.'

'Just a joke,' replied Elizabeth realising the truth of this last remark, but Angela had not finished with her critical advice. "A joke, yes, but it is also naughty because remember the subconscious mind is extremely strong and it is very powerful and don't give it words to believe what you don't want it to believe because you have a lot of work ahead of you, you have a lot to do.' Angela's words were both emphatic and stressed.

Elizabeth realised that this interview, or as Angela termed it, a conversation, was not going to let her off lightly and had become very serious indeed. 'Yes, I believe I have a lot of work ahead of me, I will do it if all is well with him.'

'Absolutely, and he is there, he is sitting there,' and she gestured towards a large easy chair opposite Elizabeth. She paused and appeared to be having some sort of short discussion with her other unseen guests. 'I think I ought to explain to Elizabeth, well... Michael came to see me over a week ago, was it?' again she seemed to be consulting with her voices, 'was it just over a week ago? When did you come? It wasn't last week; when did you come then? – Two weeks ago.'

'Long ago as that? I did not know I was coming to you...' interposed Elizabeth.

'Yes, it must have been two weeks ago, you came because last week I was flat out, that's right, that's right, it was Wednesday before last, yes it would have been then.'

'How did he know? I did not know!'

'Oh! They are way ahead of us!'

'They are!' Elizabeth by this time had become completely involved in this conversation which seemed to include several other people, and felt sufficiently emboldened to ask, 'Is it possible to ask a question?'

'Oh! Carry on!'

'I want to know if he read my last letter?'

'Yes, absolutely, yes, yes and it is actually written on his heart, he is saying it is embellished on my heart.'

Elizabeth felt overcome with emotion and love towards her unseen friend, how she wished she could see him, but she was now becoming sure that he was indeed present in this sunny room.

Angela continued...'Very much so, very very much so.'

'I found it opened...' Elizabeth briefly interposed.

'Yes, he had, he is saying. I could not take it with me physically, but I have taken it with me mentally, and it is etched on my heart, embellished.'

'So, what I feel he has reciprocated?' asked Elizabeth anxiously.

'Totally,' reassured Angela.

'I have confidence in that?' again queried Elizabeth, as always anxious to check up on her facts.

'Yes, totally,' reaffirmed Angela.

'I am not deluding myself? This is what has been bothering me.'

'The issue is there is only one reason you are here today, and it is to check whether you are in delusion; that is the only reason you are here, you are not looking for information.'

'I am not,' interposed Elizabeth.

'You are not looking for, am I doing the right thing? You are looking for whether you are in delusion. Now, all we can do through our channel is just to reach out to you and ask you to have the belief and the faith in our knowledge. You must understand that we are earthbound for such a short time, and the delusion in life is not believing there is more in the great universe.'

'I believe that, but it is such a wonderful thing, so unexpected, unimagined, so wonderful, I find it so hard to believe that all these amazing things that have been happening to me are real, I want it so much that I feel I am deluding myself out of the sheer desire for it to be so.'

'Not at all,' Angela assured her. 'We must learn to step into an area of our own being, the space within our own mind to know that there are great powers within the universe that can help us when we are ready to be helped.'

'But there is one more point I would like to make...'

'Feel free,' Angela replied.

'I do not want to interrupt you...'

'It is a conversation,' reminded Angela.

'But I feel,' resumed Elizabeth, slowly feeling her way to express clearly her strongly held convictions, 'that because I met him, and because of the way I met him, and everything that has happened between, that God has given me some special purpose, that I have a special job to do.'

Angela's short 'Absolutely' encouraged Elizabeth to continue to explore and put into words her feelings, at first faltering, but as she spoke, her words becoming clearer, not only to herself, but she hoped to those who seemed to be listening to her words.

'I feel... if I felt our meeting was meaningless...'

'No, it is...' and here Angela broke off laughing in a most natural way. 'Yes, that's right; I knew you were going to say that to me when we met before. Michael is saying that when you meet someone who just climbs into your heart and stays there you start to ask questions; why did it happen at that point? Obviously one of his first questions, why did it happen so late? But he has now realised that it happened early, because it is very difficult... give me another word.' Here she paused searching for the right words to explain, 'This was your time of meeting, and it had to be when you were in the second half of your life for you to recognise one another, but now you will go on through many lives together and have much longer...' Here Angela expressed the word, dragging it out to give added value to what she was saying...'periods together, and in that you can only have trust and faith at this time, but you will, because he is here now and this is a beginning of many long journeys that you will make together and you have now decided on a path that helps other people, it benefits other people, and that is the most important thing, and that fills Michael with enormous pride.'

Joy now flooded through Elizabeth's heart on hearing these words. 'I really want to do something to help...' she interposed, immediately followed by Angela's next words.

'Well the important thing is to be giving to anybody who is struggling to make a mark, who needs guidance to make a mark.'

'As I thought, people need nurturing, encouraging,' Elizabeth added.

'But more importantly he is saying, look around for somebody who nobody has recognised. That is why he is with you because he will, and he will prod you to see it.'

'How is he going to tell me?' asked the curious Elizabeth.

'You will just intuitively know.'

'I seem to know...'

'Yes, you will know intuitively.'

Elizabeth still struggling to clarify her thoughts and feelings continued, 'Because it has never happened before I realise all these things are coming into me, I feel he is part of me, I feel that because I am interested in… and I think that is Michael...'

'Yes he is,' confirmed Angela, 'Have you had, if not you will certainly know soon, tingling sensations like sort of warm flushing tingling sensations?'

A slightly embarrassed Elizabeth tentatively offered, 'Very hot, yes like that,' not entirely sure how to describe all these new and unfamiliar feelings. 'And other physical things, it feels like he is running... '

Angela finished for her: 'Spiders running down your spine? Yes, well that is Michael.'

'And I talk to him in my head,' responded Elizabeth feeling slightly more confident.

'Absolutely.'

'It is all right to do that, is it?'

'It is the most perfect way to work.'

'I feel as if our minds are in communication all the time.'

'They are,' affirmed Angela Elizabeth sought her confirmation by asking for a second time, 'They are?' before she was satisfied on this point by Angela's firm reply.

'You will intuitively know. Michael's one and only concern, you must learn, and yes everybody here is agreeing, you must learn to trust your intuition and don't doubt it; the minute you doubt it you will make a mistake. O.K.? Because remember, as with anything anybody in the world tries to do for good, there will be people trying to take. So that...' she paused and appeared to listen attentively. 'Yes, that's right, he is saying, I am full of joy that you are lost in the same love that I am lost in, but at the same time don't let that cloud your judgement. So please work very hard with your strong intuition and if you have any doubts get other people to help you and check things out. Do you understand?'

'Not one hundred per cent because I think it may not have happened...'

'No, yes,' Angela agreed.

'I think it may be something that's coming up. Am I right?' said Elizabeth seeking clarification on this point.

'Yes, that's right, yes.'

'Am I right?' asked Elizabeth once again.

'Yes, you are, something that's coming up.'

'Well, I hope he knows what a lovely man I think he is...' But these words were lost as Angela seemed to be listening most attentively to another conversation.

'I do beg your pardon I was just listening to someone. He's turning to talk to somebody else and I am just wondering who... another person has just walked in and I do not know who they are.'

A long pause ensued whilst Elizabeth looked enquiringly at Angela and waited attentively for her next words.

'Um... another very lovely lady over here called Eleanor...' she said slowly in explanation. 'No, no, this will all be revealed to me in a minute. We will find out what is going on here,' she again paused and then resumed, 'Yes, no, no, I wasn't... no, no, it is *your* conversation. Now, Michael is just saying a very interesting thing. He is just saying you have a very huge heart and you want to help other people, which obviously is completely and utterly applaudable by everybody here because that is what our role should be, but also, and everybody here is also saying, Michael more than anybody is saying to you, also be kind to you, take care of you because it is easy to just give, give, give, but you must take time for yourself also, you must take time to smell the roses.'

Elizabeth at this point could see herself bending down on her way to this room to smell the lovely roses in the sunny garden outside and wondered whether she had been watched by those unseen eyes as she passed by. Angela again seemed preoccupied with other conversations, and then told Elizabeth, 'There is a lot of activity going on around here at the moment, what are you all up to?'

'Did you find out about Eleanor?' asked Elizabeth, feeling somewhat left out of the conversation.

'Eleanor is obviously, sorry to interrupt you ... you obviously know each other? Ah! Eleanor moved on as a very young woman, and she learned to play the violin by touch because she is blind.'

'Did Michael teach her? 'asked the interested Elizabeth.

'Yes.'

'How wonderful!'

'And they, well I think I had better explain this afterwards, that's right, this is literally just a chance meeting, she was going by and she recognised... and that's why she was standing back waiting to be invited to come and join us. Now this appears to me to be a very significant thing that has happened that Eleanor has appeared. We are talking about the giving and the teaching and the recognising, yes, so there must be careful planning in everything that you do, and take very sound confidential advice on how you set up anything that involves anything to do with finance because you must be protected but at the same time everybody here is asking you for your faith that they will not let you trip up.'

'I appreciate that,' murmured Elizabeth by now totally lost as to the meaning of this conversation, but at the same time feeling that it would all fall into place at some future date, but there was more to come and she listened while Angela continued.

'So that if at any time you get a funny feeling about something, Michael is actually saying to you, you will get a feeling of coldness, you will get a shiver down your spine and that will be his communication to you to say just look at this, just back off, can you double check this. Just double check and that will be a sign always from him to you, please double check this. Do you understand? And also there is another element here that you may find difficult to understand, you may not particularly want to hear this right now, but it is Michael's wish and the rest of us here, you will meet another man earthbound who you will be extremely close to...'

'I don't want this,' interrupted Elizabeth swiftly, knowing in her heart that no one could possibly be a replacement for her friend so recently taken from her, but Angela continued nevertheless.

'No, but you will be extremely close and also it will be part of you to be given to Michael because Michael wants it for your protection.'

'But I do not want it to upset our relationship...'

'Nothing,' stated Angela firmly and emphatically, 'will upset your relationship to have a very close friend earthbound. It is a very beneficial thing especially if this person is going to work within the protection of you. Nobody,' and here again Angela stressed the word, 'nobody can step into your heart as he has done.'

'But that is not fair on any other man is it?'

'No, but the thing is you lay the foundations before them and you explain that you have this love, but you have a huge heart. I beg your pardon because someone here is waxing lyrical in Russian! You have a huge heart and there are still unused compartments, and there are other compartments for other people and, as you know, one can love a friend very deeply quite differently to one's soul mate, quite differently to one's child. They are all different types of love.'

'But would Michael leave me?'

'No, he will never leave you, yes, he will never leave.'

'But am I damaging Michael in any way by stopping him going on to higher things?'

'He is at higher things he is working very hard. There is not anything you can do to damage him; he has a very defined role with it, yes, within your new role. That is the best way of putting it, is it not? A very defined role. What he is very committed to is allowing the underprivileged to have a go...'

'Absolutely,' interposed Elizabeth...

'To find that, yes, that door will open for you just because you have not come from a background that has money, and it is not just about money, but it is having the people around you who believe in you and who will say yes, if you can do it, then do it.'

'I have always liked to encourage people,' added Elizabeth, still not at all sure where this conversation was going, but very glad that the tape recorder was still silently whirring round. How long this interview had already lasted she had no idea but felt that surely her hour must nearly be up and she would have to lose this precious contact with her loved one.

'Yes, and he would love for one child to come from obscurity to find their role, to find their gift, and he is saying to me right now that even if they start in music and go somewhere else, that is wonderful as music will never leave their heart.'

'That is exactly my philosophy: if you engender something and if it moves sideways, it is not wasted. It is never wasted.'

'It will not go, it was the catalyst, it was the spring board, and it was the start and his support to you if you can be the start for anybody for anything...'

'I will do it, you can be sure of that.'

'Then, well that's right; he is saying that is the biggest joy in life to be the catalyst for another.'

'Absolutely!' concurred Elizabeth heartily.

'Um, yes, that's a lovely way of putting it, when you say it like that... he is just saying, well, Eleanor is just talking to him and saying because of being blind and basically disabled she had always wanted to be famous; she wanted to be somebody, and he taught her that she was already somebody, and that she did not need to chase fame because she was famous in her own heart already, and she was famous to Our Lord who is the most important person to be famous to, and oh! Evidently Michael gave her a tiny little musical box.'

'Oh! Did he?' asked Elizabeth interested in this event which showed another side of Michael's character.

'Yes, and he told her that whenever she felt down or anxious to open the music box and that would remind her of this conversation, and she said that it always worked.'

'Lovely,' smiled Elizabeth, who always enjoyed a good story.

'And she said, whenever she felt nervous, she would open the little musical box, hear that tune and suddenly she had power, she felt strong. Oh! How lovely, it is lovely when people meet up after a long time.'

'Yes, beautiful, yes,' agreed Elizabeth, and noted that Angela had changed her position in her chair and now spoke to her directly to her

'So, let us return to the most important issue here, we will just go over one or two points with your permission...'

'Please,' acquiesced Elizabeth.

'As far as your heart and your mind will expand to the fact that we are all here, we are, there is no delusion in your life. If there had been delusion before or after you and Michael would not have met, because the meeting was designed, it was part of life's pattern, life's path, and whilst of course huge sadness weighs through emotion, of course it does, huge sadness...'

'Please forgive me for feeling huge sadness, I feel so bereft, I cannot help it at times.'

'I know, I do apologise, that's right, Michael is saying something which I agree with and everybody agrees with absolutely... What do you mean, I should tell Elizabeth what I always say? Oh! Absolutely!'

'What did you say?' thinking she already knew what Angela was about to say.

'Oh! Yes! You had a laugh about that, did you not? Everybody is reminding me I have had a similar conversation many, many times over many years, and we have talked about this issue. You have just said you were so sorry for feeling bereft, et cetera... I have always answered that if nobody cried for me, I would come back and haunt them!'

Here Elizabeth laughed, as this was a comment she had herself made at various times in the past.

Angela went on, 'and Michael is saying that to know that one person feels for another the way you felt, and obviously he apologises for this, but of course from the point that he went to, he has seen your tears, he has seen your heartache and whilst that makes his heart heavy, it also puts the sunshine in his eyes because you recognise that you were truly loved and it is also, can you understand, it is nice, it is comforting, it is loving to know you are being missed. It is important.'

'I understand; it is all so new, he said it was all so new to him, and I said it's all new to me also,' and as Elizabeth said these words she remembered their seemingly long ago, early conversations when the same thoughts had been exchanged between them over the telephone wires.

Angela continued, 'Absolutely, it is a very new thing, but yes, that is lovely, he is saying it just makes music even more poignant than it was before.'

'Yes, it is very poignant. When I hear lovely music, I think immediately he is there.'

'He is listening to you; I do not need to tell you he is listening to every word you say.'

'He is there in the music,' explained Elizabeth.

'Absolutely,' confirmed Angela, and went on to say before Elizabeth could continue – 'I am so sorry, everybody here is talking. Gosh, you have a lot of work to do, haven't you? You are going to be looking at a base for everything to happen from, and also the organisation, the organising of other people, you are going to end up like a teacher, teaching teachers...'

'It is hard to believe,' said an astonished Elizabeth.

'But when you start with an idea that is locked in passion it takes on a different personality and then you must start to plan how to put it into action, so one making lists, start to create a business plan for the rest of your life, start to make a plan where do you want this idea to go.'

Elizabeth, overwhelmed with this startling turn in the conversation, feebly interrupted, 'it has not come yet.'

'No, but if you are going to create an environment for people to come and spend a week, two weeks...'

'This is beginning to fit a bit,' said Elizabeth, trying to see her way.

'However long they are going to come to stay you are going to bring in other people who are talented to help these people...' Again, Elizabeth prepared to join in but Angela now in full flow, continued, 'so you will need to resource and source these people.'

'I had hoped Michael was going to help with this,' responded Elizabeth, now thoroughly out of her depth, desperately trying to understand this almost continuous flow of information and advice, but Angela had more to say.

'So you don't want people who are just good at playing a violin or playing a piano; you want people with a heart who are prepared to give time or give time cheaply or see it as a dual activity, that they go to a lovely place in the world and it is not a sabbatical for them to lift and give. You'll need to create a directory and a 52 week planner showing who will be available for when, and for what instrument, and for whatever; and also do not be afraid, once you are gathering your ideas, to start researching and finding out where you can get funding, because projects that are to serve the community deserve to be funded. So, make sure you spend careful time sitting, in the beginning do not try to organise it, just get all the ideas and all the information down in any form, and then start to sort it out afterwards. We will be behind you; Michael will be at your side.'

Elizabeth, now completely overwhelmed, and seeking to find some sort of connecting thread with her original conversation with Michael on the train, asked, 'Can I ask, does it come out of our original conversation?'

'Yes! Yes!' emphatically replied Angela.

'It does?' asked Elizabeth, still not sure of her ground.

'It does,' again Angela affirmed.

'As I thought, I do not see a way at all at the moment.'

Angela, seeking to reassure her, said 'That is why everybody is saying to you, start to get stuff down on paper; commit the words to paper, start to talk to Education Authorities, do research.'

'Pretty frightening idea, all this.'

'But the thing, you see, is many people in this world have let good ideas go because they assume someone else is doing it...'

'I know...' joined in Elizabeth.

'Or they assume, if someone else is not doing it, it cannot be done, or if someone else is not doing it, there is no way of finding the money. Well, as we all know, that is poppycock because if there is a diamond in the heart for giving, there is always a route there, there is always a path to make that happen, and yes... and everybody here... Michael is saying, and remember no man is an island. Don't try and do everything on your own.'

A somewhat relieved Elizabeth responded, 'That's what I wanted to hear.' Angela continued, 'Don't be frightened of, first and foremost, working with your intuition because that is your guide. Everybody here is coming through you, so be very focused on trusting your intuition. Talk to as many people as possible, explain that you are interested in them, and that they have knowledge you can garner from them. Tell them you trust them if at any time you get a quirky feeling about the trusting of them, back off, you will get the ice-cold shiver and that will be Michael.'

Without irony, Elizabeth said, 'Thank you Michael' Angela continued, 'They have to develop a way of communication, I mean we talk on the energy lines. It is no different to a telephone except it...'

'It is mind to mind,' popped in Elizabeth, like a good pupil catching on to the principle of the lesson.

'Yes, it is mind to mind, mind to mind is more powerful than the mouth. It is much more powerful.'

'Oh! Yes!'

'Um, but sometimes we all know here, and obviously Michael is learning now, or is being taught, that everybody on this side sometimes has to develop other techniques just to make sure someone is listening, and so of course if you are very tied up in an idea, in excitement it can be very easy to forget to really listen to your intuition, and you can go bowling along, so very often they will develop a technique which says "hang on," (here there was heard knocking sound outside) "so, unfortunately or fortunately, whichever way you look at it, you are going to get a cold shiver, it is as simple as that, it is another technique.'

Elizabeth now felt that she herself should make a commitment to Michael and told the apparent listeners, 'I have committed myself to listening to him, I told him this a day or two ago, I am trusting him completely to take me down a path which is going to be beneficial in this sort of action, and I have given him my total trust.'

Angela agreed, 'Absolutely, yes.'

Elizabeth, now getting into her stride in this conversation continued, 'Because I think it is so important.'

'It is very very important, and of course you are going to get to know a lot of people, and you are going to need to talk to a lot of people, but the most important thing is to decide on a start point and move gradually rather than trying to race through and run and do too much too quickly.'

'I do not think I would do that,' reassured Elizabeth. 'I am pretty cautious actually, and, I do not have the facilities at the moment to do anything...' 'But you will be needing to write a lot of letters, you will be helped in your mind to mind communication of how to formulate that successfully, and Michael is asking you, please do not be distraught or put off when you get hoity-toity letters back. They go straight in the bin as that proves they have not got a heart, but never be disillusioned because there are many people out there who will find it a joy to give to other people.'

There was a short pause whilst Angela seemed to be listening attentively to her other voices, and as she turned once more towards Elizabeth said, 'That is a very good point... he is also saying, and please don't forget that music is a wonderful communicating tool for some people who are locked in emotional pain, and for those who can discover their youth in old age.'

Elizabeth decided to make a joke of these last words, 'I wonder what he means by that. You are pulling my leg, oh dear, such a fun person to be with...'

'He still is.'

'He exists to me,' replied Elizabeth.

'It is just a different way of communicating that is right, pure and simple, yes absolutely.'

There then followed a long pause when Angela appeared to be listening attentively, her head tilted to one side... 'What is that piece of music?' she asked softly. 'It's beautiful, it is absolutely beautiful.'

Now with growing certainty Elizabeth asked, 'I want to know the name, I have forgotten...'

Angela enquired again, 'What is this piece of music? It is absolutely beautiful. Mendelssohn... It is gorgeous, ah! A tear is running down Eleanor's face, no stop it, you will get me going in a minute...'

It was at this moment that Elizabeth knew with complete certainty that Michael had not left her, as this was the piece of music he had dedicated to her on that never to be forgotten visit that spring.

After a pause, Angela collected herself and once again focused on the practical issues – 'So, let us look at a possibility, a property with rooms, obviously, where people can come to stay for short or long periods; they can come to stay, not just to learn a craft but to find something within themselves.'

'To have rest and peace,' added Elizabeth.

'To have tranquillity and escape, because we all need to escape to gather our energies in order to survive, and that is what many of the people that come to you that is what they need, they need rebuilding, to discover something through another medium of music.'

At this point Elizabeth became aware that Angela was tiring, and as if in response to this thought, Angela appeared to try and bring this remarkable series of conversations to some kind of conclusion and went on to say, 'They have got some points they want to go through so you are being asked to do thorough research, but never be perturbed or put out because all the right doors will open and they will open at the right time. Make sure you gather two or three very trusted people around you to support you, and the last and most important thing or two – you have a habit of that, you start to say one thing and there are half a dozen bits in it, yes...' Elizabeth laughed as Angela continued, 'It is a bit like, yes, that's right, it is a bit like starting with one sheet of paper and ending up with a whole notepad, yes, right, OK, come on then, right, we will with your permission Michael, I am going to say to Elizabeth this is the final thing, but it is part A B C D E F, yes,' she said laughing, 'OK part one, I am not gone, I am beside you, I am with you and we will do this together.'

Again, Elizabeth was happy to say, 'That is what I wanted to hear,' as Angela continued.

'We will do this together. It will be a great joy and satisfaction for me. I want you to take careful time on the research, and talk a lot to people in different organisations about finding funding to help you, as everyone here has said to you, protect yourself.'

Elizabeth could not help adding, 'Pray God I have the strength at my age.' She was immediately reassured. 'You have plenty of energy and plenty of strength.'

'Thank you,' she replied laughing, not entirely convinced on this point.

'Yes, and also, that's right, working from a point of joy gives us a greater energy; and finally, everyone here is saying for Michael to have the last word, normally this lot do, yes, it makes it a change for you not to have the last word. Everyone here is saying it has been an absolute delight to sit with you and talk with you, they applaud your journey. You will be supported and protected, but the final word is going to be left with Michael, and Michael says all I have to say to you at this time is my heart is yours.'

With her own heart filled with love, Elizabeth responded, 'It gives me great joy, very great joy. It will enable me to go on.'

At this point Angela got up from her chair saying, 'Well, he is going to ask me to do one thing before we leave, so, if you will excuse me I have got to get up, and, crossing the room to the chair opposite Elizabeth, she bent forward, placing her hand on the lips of the unseen guest and returned to place her fingers on Elizabeth's lips, saying, 'from his lips to your lips'.

Now Elizabeth realised, fully and completely, that life was indeed immortal and she would be with Michael for the rest of her life and beyond. This was his legacy left to her… his gift of love.

Chapter XVII

Reprise

Elizabeth continued to muse on the past events which had led her to this day, and this journey to meet her new grandchild. At first she had been so very aware of mentally referring back to the meeting with Angela and all the information she had been given and had tried to tailor her progress accordingly. However, her first decision had been to take a year off from all her other work and use the time to make a thorough search into the subject of music and musical education. As time passed, she soon became aware of the plight of many children who had either multiple or serious life-limiting disabilities, who needed some new kind of help to make their lives more bearable and sustainable.

Her time during this year of research became more like a detective novel; she followed one clue then another. As she was passed from one new source of information to the next, she found that people were willing to give her their time and expertise, ready to assist her in her quest to find her path, to bring Michael's hopes and dreams to fulfilment.

As she mused during her train journey today, she realised how many of the guidelines she had been given on that memorable day had come to fruition. She never ceased to be astonished how events, even years later, suddenly and most naturally developed, without any deliberate intention on her part, to fit in with Michael's suggestions or wishes. Even today, she was on the brink of moving her charity, which had been founded to help children, into another new and exciting era, foreseen by Michael.

The comfort and strength that Michael gave her, and the knowledge that he was there guiding and helping her in what was, and is, probably the biggest adventure of her life, enabled her to have the courage to fulfil his dreams.

FINIS